Core Knowledge Language Arts®

Unit 4
Workbook

Skills Strand
GRADE 1

Amplify learning.

Core Knowledge®

ISBN 978-1-61700-203-8

Printed in the USA
08 LSCOW 2021

Unit 4
Workbook

This Workbook contains worksheets that accompany many of the lessons from the Teacher Guide for Unit 4. Each worksheet is identified by the lesson number in which it is used. Some of the worksheets in this book do not include written instructions for students because the instructions would have contained nondecodable words. The expectation is that teachers will explain these worksheets to students orally, using the guidelines in the Teacher Guide. Nondecodable instructions are also included along the side of each of these worksheets, and are meant to be read aloud by a teacher or family member. The Workbook is a student component, which means each student should have a Workbook.

Dear Family Member,

Today our class started the Unit 4 of the Core Knowledge Language Arts program. The Reader for this unit is called *The Green Fern Zoo*. Your child will bring home stories you can read together about zoo keeper Vern and the different types of animals he cares for at the Green Fern Zoo. Remember that reading at home with your child is important for their success as a reader.

In addition, your child's spelling words for this week include the days of the week. Students will practice writing the date, including the days of the week. All of the spelling words this week are Tricky Words. Tricky Words do not play by the rules, meaning there are spellings that do not sound the way students would expect them to. These words need to be memorized, so your child will benefit from practice reading and writing them.

1. Monday

2. Tuesday

3. Wednesday

4. Thursday

5. Friday

6. Saturday

7. Sunday

8. would

Directions: Have students trace and copy the digraph and words. Students should say the sounds while writing the letters.

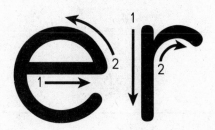

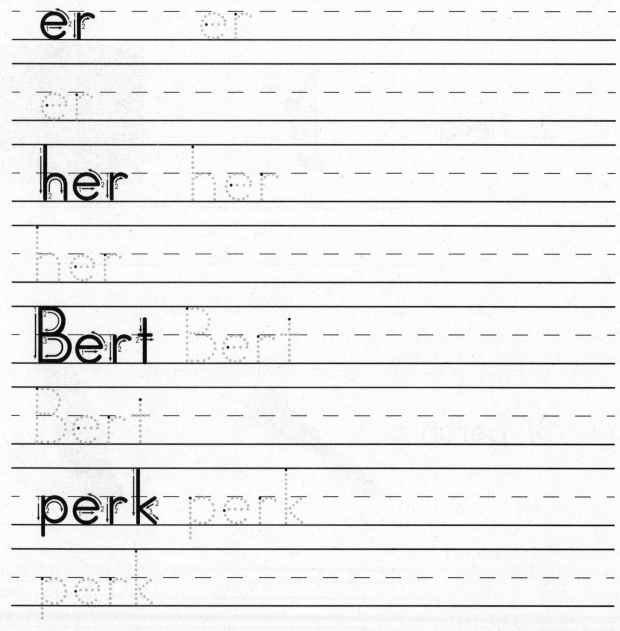

er   er

her   her

Bert   Bert

perk   perk

Print the words on the lines where they fit best.

1. fe**r**n

_____   _____

- - - - - - - - - - - - -   - - - - - - - - - - - - -

_____   _____

2. h**er**d

_____   _____

- - - - - - - - - - - - -   - - - - - - - - - - - - -

_____   _____

3. p**er**ch

_____   _____

- - - - - - - - - - - - -   - - - - - - - - - - - - -

_____   _____

~~f**er**n~~	~~r**a**t~~
r**u**st	p**er**ch
r**o**pe	r**a**g
cl**er**k	v**er**b
r**oo**m	t**er**m

/r/ as in <u>r</u>ed

/er/ as in h<u>er</u>

rat

fern

Dear Family Member,

Your child has been taught to read words with the vowel digraph, or letter team, 'er' as in *her*. To practice this new spelling, ask your child to cut out the word cards below. In addition to the 'er' spelling, some of the words below are Tricky Words and previously taught spellings. Have your child read all of the words aloud, and arrange the cards to make phrases such "the herd" and "one fern." You may also ask your child to copy the phrases onto a sheet of paper. Please keep the cards for future practice.

the	all	big
herd	clerk	perch
food	book	one
pound	coin	hawk

her	clerk	round	coin
v**er**b	paws	scoops	food

Directions: Have students read each sentence and write the word from the word box that best fits the sentence.

1. The plate is _____.

2. The _____ gave h**er** a dime.

3. Dogs have _____.

4. I would like three _____!

Directions: Have students read each sentence and write the word from the word box that best fits the sentence.

her	clerk	round	coin
verb	paws	scoops	food

5. I can cook a lot of _____.

6. _____ dad is at home.

7. I will flip a _____.

8. Is this word a _____?

Meet Vern

1. <u>Where</u> will **Ve**rn take you?

   o   the shop

   o   the Green **Fe**rn Zoo

   o   the bus

Page _____

2. What is **Ve**rn's job?

- -

- -

- -

Directions: Have students reread the story and answer the questions.

3. What could be some things with wings?

_____

- - - - - - - - - - - - - - - - -

_____

- - - - - - - - - - - - - - - - -

_____

- - - - - - - - - - - - - - - - -

_____

4. Name some things that you could see at the zoo.

_____

- - - - - - - - - - - - - - - - -

_____

- - - - - - - - - - - - - - - - -

_____

- - - - - - - - - - - - - - - - -

_____

ar   ar

ar

art   art

art

farm   farm

farm

yarn   yarn

yarn

Print the words on the lines where they fit best.

1. **ar**m

a̤r̤m̤

2. c**ar**

3. st**ar**

4. y**ar**n

5. c**ar**t

Dear Family Member,

Your child has been taught to read words with the vowel digraphs 'er' as in *her*, and 'ar' as in *car*. Ask your child to cut out the word cards. Have your child arrange the cards to make phrases or sentences. You may also ask your child to copy the phrases or sentences on the sheet of paper. Please keep the cards for future practice.

verb	herd	perch
the	march	one
yard	a	green
farm	chart	fern
this	big	is
stars	tree	bark

Spelling Test

1. _____

2. _____

3. _____

4. _____

5. _____

6. _____

7. _____

8. _____

Things That Swim

1. What is a trout?

   ○ a dog

   ○ a bug

   ○ a fish

Page_____

2. What **par**ts of a trout help it hide?

   ○ spots and m**ar**ks

   ○ mouth and teeth

   ○ fins and scales

Page _____

3. What big fish makes wee fish run and hide?

○ trout

○ reef sh**ar**k

○ squid

Page _____

4. <u>Why</u> d<u>o</u> reef sh**ar**ks make th<u>eir</u> home close to reefs?

_____

- - - - - - - - - - - - - - - - - -

_____

- - - - - - - - - - - - - - - - - -

_____

- - - - - - - - - - - - - - - - - -

_____

5. What d<u>o</u> reef sh**ar**ks like to feed on?

- - - - - - - - - - - - - - - - - -

_____

- - - - - - - - - - - - - - - - - -

_____

- - - - - - - - - - - - - - - - - -

_____

Page _____

Dear Family Member,

This is a story your child has probably read once, possibly several times, at school. Encourage your child to read the story to you and then talk about it together. Note that the tricky parts in Tricky Words are underlined in gray, and the new sound-spellings in this unit are bolded.

Repeated oral reading is an important way to improve reading skills. It can be fun for your child to repeatedly read this story to a friend, relative, or even a pet.

Meet Vern

My name is V**er**n, and I have the best job! My job is to take you kids in to see the Green F**er**n Zoo.

We will see things with wings and things with scales, things that bite and things that sting, things that creep and things that swim.

I have lots of fun facts and tales to share with you. So let's see the zoo and have some fun!

Name _____

TAKE HOME

Dear Family Member,

Your child's spelling words for this week include the 'er', 'ar', and 'or' spellings that your child has been learning in this unit. Your child should practice reading and writing these words. The last spelling word is a Tricky Word. Tricky Words do not play by the rules, meaning there are spellings that do not sound the way students would expect them to. These words need to be memorized.

Spelling Words Lesson 6

1. sharp

2. fern

3. start

4. spoil

5. verb

6. shark

7. crawl

8. Tricky Word: because

Directions: Have students read the words in the box and write each word in the sentence where the word fits best.

st**ar**s	p**er**k	look	f**er**n	shout
oil	claws	moon	sh**ar**k	h**er**d

1. There is not a _____ in this lake.

2. The **car** needs _____ in it.

3. That cat has sh**ar**p _____ !

4. The flag has _____ and stripes.

5. My mom had to ask us not to _____ .

stars	perk	look	fern	shout
oil	claws	moon	shark	herd

6. She must _____ up and not sleep!

7. I saw a _____ of deer in the woods.

8. I would like to see the Green _____ Zoo.

9. _____ at that big wave!

10. We look up at the stars and the _____ when it gets dark.

Directions: Have students read the words in the box and write each word in the sentence where the word fits best.

it is   he's

here is   can't

she is   she's

can not   it's

Directions: Have students match the words to their contracted form.

he is   here's

can't	let's	here's
she's	it's	B**er**t's

1. _____ sad.

2. _____ hot out.

3. _____ run to the p**ar**k.

4. _____ a good pal.

5. _____ my class.

6. We _____ see the sh**ar**ks.

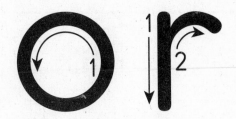

or   or

or

corn   corn

corn

fork   fork

fork

short short

short

In the box are six words. Print them on the lines where they fit best.

st**or**k	f**or**k	th**or**ns
c**or**n	sh**or**ts	c**or**d

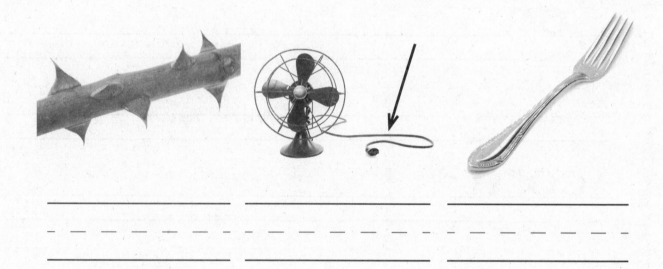

_____

- - - - - - - - - - -

_____

_____

- - - - - - - - - - -

_____

Dear Family Member,

Your child has been learning to read and write contractions. Work with your child to write each sentence with the contracted form of the words in parentheses. Extension: Use contractions orally with your child, pausing to discuss the formation of the contracted form.

TAKE HOME

1. _____ glad we can have
(he is)

cake.

2. _____ with h**er** gran.
(she is)

3. _____ run to the p**ar**k!
(let us)

4. I _____ ride a bike.
(can not)

5. _____ the book!
(here is)

Directions: Have students copy the word onto the left side of the paper, fold it in half, and then write the word from memory on the right side of the paper.

1. _____

2. _____

3. _____

4. _____

5. _____

6. _____

7. _____

8. _____

9. _____

10. _____

1. _____

2. _____

3. _____

4. _____

5. _____

6. _____

7. _____

8. _____

9. _____

10. _____

Dear Family Member,

This is a story your child has probably read once, possibly several times, at school. Encourage your child to read the story to you and then talk about it together. The tricky parts in tricky words are underlined in gray. Please note that the multi-syllable words that students encounter in the Readers and Workbook will be divided between syllables with a dot. This dot serves as an early cue to assist students in chunking words, and will be omitted in later units.

Repeated oral reading is an important way to improve reading skills. It can be fun for your child to repeatedly read this story to a friend, relative, or even a pet.

Things That Swim

I hope you kids like things that swim, be·cause this is the room where we keep all the fish.

The fish here are trout. A trout is a fish that swims in cool lakes and creeks. You can see that they have lots of spots and marks. The spots and marks help the trout hide. They make the trout look a lot like the sand on the bed of a creek.

Here's a big fish that makes all of the wee fish run and hide. This is a reef shark. It has that name be·cause it likes to make its home close to a reef, where there are lots of fish.

You can see that the reef shark has fins and a set of gills on its side. You can not see them from here, but this shark has lots of sharp teeth in its mouth.

Would a reef shark bite you? Well, you are not the lunch that this shark would like best. A reef shark likes to feed on squid, crabs, and shrimp. But it would be smart not to get the reef shark mad at you all the same!

Chimps

1. Green **Fer**n Zoo has _____ chimps.

   ○ one

   ○ five

   ○ ten

2. <u>Who</u> is Bess?

   ○ a chimp

   ○ V**er**n's pal

   ○ a sh**ar**k

3. What d<u>o</u> chimps not like to munch on?

   ○ plants

   ○ seeds

   ○ rocks

Directions: Have students reread the story and answer the questions.

4. What will **Bar**t have **for** lunch?

_____

- -

_____

- -

_____

5. What will Max do **for** fun?

_____

- -

_____

- -

_____

6. Why were **Car**l and **Nor**m not pals last week?

_____

- -

_____

- -

_____

Mandrills

1. Is a male man·drill's nose green?

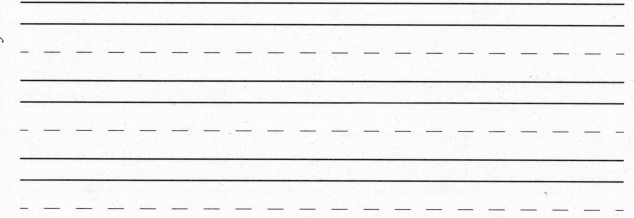

2. What makes man·drills look and feel good?

3. What is the **verb** in, "We feed man·drills ants, grass·es, nuts, **bar**k, plant shoots, and roots."

- ○ man·drills
- ○ feed
- ○ **bar**k

4. List 4 nouns that you found in "Man·drills."

_____

_____

_____

_____

Directions: On a separate sheet of paper, have students illustrate one of the nouns from the story.

Dear Family Member,

This is a story your child has probably read once, possibly several times, at school. Encourage your child to read the story to you and then talk about it together. The tricky parts in Tricky Words are underlined in gray. Please note that the multi-syllable words are divided between syllables with a dot. This dot serves as a cue to assist students in chunking syllables, and will be omitted in later units.

Repeated oral reading is an important way to improve reading skills. It can be fun for your child to repeatedly read this story to a friend, relative, or even a pet.

Chimps

Next, let's see the chimps. We have ten chimps here at the Green Fern Zoo. You can see them all out there if you look hard.

The one you see here is Bess. She has a snack in her mouth. Bess and the rest of the chimps like to munch on plants, nuts, and seeds.

Do you see that chimp with the stick? That's Bart. Bart likes to have ants for lunch. To get the ants, he takes a stick and sticks it in an ant hill. Then he lifts it up

and licks off the ants. Yum, yum!

The chimp with the rope in his hand is Max. He's just a babe. He was born in March. Bess is his mom.

Max is a lot of fun. He likes to swing on the rope and splash in the pool.

The two chimps up on the rocks are Carl and Norm. Carl is the one on the left. Carl and Norm are pals. But they were not pals last week.

Last week we gave them a branch from a fig tree for lunch. Norm took the branch and ran off with it. He ate all of the figs. Carl was mad at Norm all week.

But that was last week. This week the two of them are pals.

Dear Family Member,

Our class has begun reading and writing two-syllable words. The spelling words this week are two-syllable words which may be more challenging than the previous one-syllable words. Your child may find it helpful to practice writing and remembering the spelling words syllable by syllable.

Spelling Words Lesson 11

1. zipper

2. barking

3. perfume

4. morning

5. carpet

6. forest

7. border

8. Tricky Word: today

Mark the words that are said and print them on the lines.

1. **ar**m·pit   **ar**t·ist   _____

2. sneez·ing   sniff·ing   _____

3. bas·kets   bask·ing   _____

4. nap·kin   napp·ing   _____

5. broil·ing   boil·ing   _____

6. twist·**er**   tweez·**er**

7. un·like   un·less

8. c**or**·n**er**   c**or**·net

9. win·**ter**   winn·**er**

10. ant·hill   ant·**ler**

Dear Family Member,

Your child has been taught to read words with the vowel digraphs 'er' as in *her*, 'ar' as in *car*, and 'or' as in *for*. Ask your child to cut out the word cards. Show the cards to your child and have your child read them. Then have your child read the word cards from previous take-home worksheets. Extension: Ask your child to copy the words onto a sheet of paper. Further extension: Read the words aloud and have your child write the words down, one sound at a time, paying attention to the vowel digraphs. Please keep the cards for future practice.

herd	storm	farm
start	clerk	born
term	sports	park
short	parts	her

1. The (pig) sn**or**ts.

2. The dog b**ar**ks.

3. The c**ar** stops.

4. The sh**ar**k hunt·ed.

5. The man helped.

_____

- - - - - - - - - - - - - - - - -

_____

- - - - - - - - - - - - - - - - -

_____

- - - - - - - - - - - - - - - - -

_____

- - - - - - - - - - - - - - - - -

_____

Directions: Have students read the sentences, circle the nouns, and underline the verbs with a squiggly line. Then have students write a few original sentences on the lines.

Things with Wings

1. The puff·in makes his home _____

    ○ in hot lands

    ○ up n**or**th

    ○ in the grass

Page _____

2. The puff·in's feet help him _____

    ○ swim

    ○ sleep

    ○ get a snack

Page _____

Directions: Have students reread the story and answer the questions.

3. What can a puff·in use to get fish?

- ○ his feet
- ○ his eggs
- ○ his bill

Page _____

4. Puff·ins are b**or**n from _____.

The puff·in mom and _____ sit

on th<u>ei</u>r egg. In the end, the _____

pops out of the shell.

5. What can a finch use to get food?

_____

- -

_____

- -

_____

Dear Family Member,

This is a story your child has probably read once, possibly several times, at school. Encourage your child to read the story to you and then talk about it together. The tricky parts in Tricky Words are underlined in gray. Please note that the multi-syllable words are divided between syllables with a dot. This dot serves as a cue to assist students in chunking syllables, and will be omitted in later units.

Repeated oral reading is an important way to improve reading skills. It can be fun for your child to repeatedly read this story to a friend, relative, or even a pet.

Mandrills

Here you can see two man·drills. Man·drills are a lot like chimps.

Do you like the red nose? The man·drill with the red nose is a male.

The man·drill on the left is groom·ing the male with the red nose. She is look·ing **for** ticks and bugs. Man·drills like groom·ing be·cause it makes them look good and feel good, too.

Look! One of the man·drills is yawn·ing! You can see that he has long, sh**ar**p teeth. Those sh**ar**p teeth help him chop up his food.

Man·drills like a lot of foods. We feed our man·drills ants, grass, nuts, b**ar**k, plant shoots, and roots.

Man·drills have sacks in·side th<u>ei</u>r cheeks. They can stuff food in the sacks and keep it there un·til they need a snack. Then they pop the food out and munch on it!

Directions: Have students underline the past-tense marker 'ed' in each verb. Then have students write the past-tense verbs that end in /ed/ under the /ed/ header, the verbs that end in /d/ under the /d/ header, and the verbs that end in /t/ under the /t/ header.

start**ed**	grinn**ed**	help**ed**	sound·ed	form**ed**	park**ed**
point·ed	smil**ed**		bak**ed**	wav**ed**	hik**ed**
lift·ed					

/ed/   /d/   /t/

Dear Family Member,

Your child has been learning about contractions, nouns, and verbs. For the first part of this worksheet, have your child circle the nouns in the sentence, and underline the verbs with a squiggly line. Review with your child that a noun is a person, place, or thing, and a verb is a word that shows action. Please note that the number of nouns in each sentence is noted in parentheses. For the second part, have your child draw a line to match the words with its contraction.

1. The (cat) naps in the (yard). (2)

2. The cook made a cake. (2)

3. The kid rides a bike to the p**ar**k. (3)

4. The tree shakes. (1)

5. A big dog b**ar**ks. (1)

it is

there's

there is

she's

let us

it's

here is

let's

she is

here's

Directions: Have students match the words to their contracted forms.

Directions: For each word, have students circle and count the spellings, then write the number of sounds in the box and copy the word on the lines. For an extra challenge, ask students to write the number of syllables in the circle.

1. ham·st**er**   6   hamster   ②

2. green   ☐   ◯

3. win·t**er**   ☐   ◯

4. slime   ☐   ◯

5. good   ☐   ◯

6. g**ar**·lic   ☐   ◯

7. shout   ☐   ◯

8. **paws**

9. **pop·corn**

10. **camp·ers**

11. **mon·ster**

12. **woods**

13. **for·get**

14. **zipp·ers**

Yes or No?

1. Is green slime a good food?

2. Do g**a**r·lic and a rose smell the same?

3. D**o** cats have paws?

4. Is a pum·pkin black?

5. Can a pig ride a bike?

6. Is pop·c**or**n a good snack?

7.   Do c**a**mp·**er**s sleep in tents?

8.   Is a v**er**b a word?

9.   W**ou**ld you like to win a prize?

10.   Can a dog tell time?

11.   Is it hot in the win·**ter**?

12.   Do c**o**ins have zipp·**er**s?

Big Cats

1. Name three things that a bob·cat hunts.

_____
- -
_____
- -
_____
- -
_____

2. Why should you not keep a bob·cat in your home?

_____
- -
_____
- -
_____
- -
_____
- -
_____
- -
_____

Directions: Have students reread the story and answer the questions.

3. What helps a pan·th**er** hunt?

_____

- -

_____

- -

_____

- -

_____

- -

_____

4. A pan·th**er** can be . . .

○ green with stripes.

○ black **or** tan, **or** can have spots.

○ red with tan dots.

Groundhogs

1. What do ground·hogs use their claws for?

_____

- -

_____

_____

_____

2. Why do ground·hogs have to be on the look·out when they are not in their holes?

_____

- -

_____

_____

_____

Directions: Have students reread the story and answer the questions.

3. <u>Where</u> was Pepp·**er** when she got out fr<u>o</u>m h**er** pen?

_____

- -

_____

- -

_____

- -

_____

4. What did Pepp·**er** stuff h**er**·self with?

_____

- -

_____

- -

_____

- -

_____

Dear Family Member,

    The spelling words for this week are two-syllable words that contain the 'er', 'ar', and 'or' spelling. Your child can practice reading and writing these words, as well as clap the syllables for them. The last spelling word is a Tricky Word. Tricky Words do not play by the rules, meaning there are spellings that do not sound the way students would expect them to. These words need to be memorized.

Spelling Words Lesson 16

1.   sounded

2.   lifted

3.   pointed

4.   parked

5.   waved

6.   grinned

7.   tripped

8.   Tricky Word: have

The Reptile Room

1. What do **gar·ter** snakes feed on?

_____

- - - - - - - - - - - - - - - - - - - -

_____

- - - - - - - - - - - - - - - - - - - -

_____

- - - - - - - - - - - - - - - - - - - -

_____

2. <u>Why</u> are **gar·ter** snakes **harm·less** **for** us?

_____

- - - - - - - - - - - - - - - - - - - -

_____

- - - - - - - - - - - - - - - - - - - -

_____

- - - - - - - - - - - - - - - - - - - -

_____

- - - - - - - - - - - - - - - - - - - -

_____

- - - - - - - - - - - - - - - - - - - -

_____

Directions: Have students reread the story and answer the questions.

3. A ratt·**ler** has a patt·**er**n on his scales so that…

_____

- -

_____

- -

_____

- -

_____

- -

_____

4. <u>Why</u> is a ratt·**ler** not h**ar**m·less f**or** us?

_____

- -

_____

- -

_____

- -

_____

- -

_____

1. To·d<u>ay</u> kids m**ar**ch in line.

2. Yes·**ter**·d<u>ay</u> kids m**ar**ched in line.

3. To·m<u>orr</u>·<u>ow</u> kids will m**ar**ch in line.

4. To·d<u>ay</u> the cat naps on the **car**·pet.

5. Yes·**ter**·d<u>ay</u> the cat napped on the **car**·pet.

6. To·m<u>orr</u>·<u>ow</u> the cat will nap on the **car**·pet.

7. To·d<u>ay</u> the man bikes at the p**ar**k.

8. Yes·**ter**·d<u>ay</u> the man biked at the p**ar**k.

9. To·m<u>orr</u>·<u>ow</u> the man will bike at the p**ar**k.

Directions: For each sentence, have students circle the nouns and underline the verbs with a squiggly line.

Dear Family Member,

Your child has been practicing reading two-syllable words. Below are two sections from a story about reptiles at the Green Fern Zoo. Have your child read the story and fill in the blank with the correct word.

| critt·**ers** | **gar**·ter | harm·less | kill·**er** |

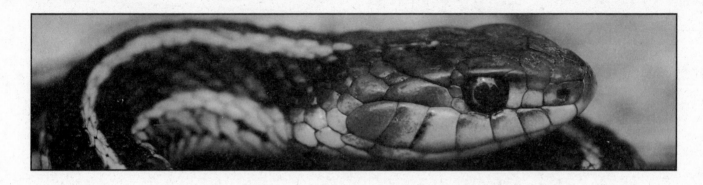

This is a _____ snake. **Gar·**ter

snakes feed on slugs, in·sects, and frogs. **For**

those _____ , the **gar·ter** snake is

a _____ . A **gar·ter** snake could

bite you, but its bite w<u>ou</u>ld not make you sick. **For**

us, a **gar·ter** snake is _____ .

| dwell·**er** | patt·**ern** | des·**ert** | ratt·**ler** |

This is a _____. A ratt·**ler** is a

des·**er**t _____ that hunts f**or**

rats and rabb·its. He has a _____ on his

scales that helps him blend in and hide in the

_____ sands. When the ratt·**ler**

is hidd·en, it is h**ar**d f**or** rats and rabb·its to see

him.

Dear Family Member,

This is a story your child has probably read once, possibly several times, at school. Encourage your child to read the story to you and then talk about it together. The tricky parts in Tricky Words are underlined in gray. Please note that the multi-syllable words are divided between syllables with a dot. This dot serves as a cue to assist students in chunking syllables, and will be omitted in later units.

Repeated oral reading is an important way to improve reading skills. It can be fun for your child to repeatedly read this story to a friend, relative, or even a pet.

Things With Wings

Next, let's see some things with wings.

This is a puff·in. He makes his home up north, not too far from the North Pole.

Look at those cute feet! But they are not just cute. The puff·in's feet help him swim.

Note, as well, his big bill. The puff·in can use his bill to get fish.

Puff·ins are b**or**n fr<u>o</u>m eggs.
The puff·in mom and dad sit on
th<u>eir</u> egg. The mom sits. Then the
dad sits. In the end, the chick
pops out of the shell. The mom
and dad take care of the chick
un·til it can care f**or** it·self. Look!
That puff·in has fish in h**er** bill! She
will feed those fish to h**er** chick.

In this next room, we have a
finch. Un·like the puff·in, the finch
makes a home in wood·lands.
He can use his bill to snap up
grass seeds f**or** food.

I'm sad to tell you that the
finch is gett·ing to be quite rare.
We are proud to have five of
them here at the Green F**er**n
Zoo.

Directions: Have students underline the past-tense marker 'ed' in each word. Then have students write the final sound(s) in each word in the slashes. Then have students write the past-tense verbs that end in /ed/ under the /ed/ header, the verbs that end in /d/ under the /d/ header, and the verbs that end in /t/ under the /t/ header.

start·ed /ed/   grinned /d/   helped /t/   marched / /   add·ed / /

seemed / /   snort·ed / /   wished / /   rubbed / /

/t/

/d/

/ed/

Termites

1. What are **ter**·mites?

_____
- - - - - - - - - - - - - - - - - - -
_____
- - - - - - - - - - - - - - - - - - -
_____
_____

2. What is in·side a **ter**·mite mound?

_____
- - - - - - - - - - - - - - - - - - -
_____
- - - - - - - - - - - - - - - - - - -
_____
- - - - - - - - - - - - - - - - - - -
_____
- - - - - - - - - - - - - - - - - - -

3. What do **ter**·mites look like?

_____

- -

_____

- -

_____

- -

_____

- -

_____

4. <u>Why</u> w<u>ou</u>ld a **ter**·mite munch on y<u>our</u> home?

_____

- -

_____

- -

_____

- -

_____

- -

_____

Name _____

Spelling Test

1. _____

2. _____

3. _____

4. _____

5. _____

6. _____

7. _____

8. _____

In the box are six words. Print them on the lines where they fit best.

g**ar**·lic	dinn·**er**	cool·**er**
hamm·**er**	jump·**er**	h**or**·net

_____

_____

_____

_____

In the box are six words. Print them on the lines where they fit best.

blend·**er**   pop·**c**o**r**n   num·**b**e**r**

car·pet   **for**·est   **gar**·den

_____   _____   _____
- - - - - - - - - - -   - - - - - - - - - - -   - - - - - - - - - - -
_____   _____   _____

48

_____   _____   _____
- - - - - - - - - - -   - - - - - - - - - - -   - - - - - - - - - - -
_____   _____   _____

Name _____

TAKE HOME

Check the Draft
Step by Step

1. Check that the name of the thing is there.	
2. Check that you des·cribed what it looks like.	
3. Check that you des·cribed the feel, sound, and taste of the thing.	
4. Check that you end·ed with a fun fact **or** if you like the thing.	
5. Aa, Bb, Cc	
6. ? . !	
7. Check that the words are spelled well.	

River Otters

1. What do riv·**er** ott·**er**s like to do?

    _____
    - - - - - - - - - - - - - - - - - - -
    _____
    - - - - - - - - - - - - - - - - - - -
    _____
    - - - - - - - - - - - - - - - - - - -
    _____

2. Which is NOT the riv·**er** ott·**er**s' home?

    ○   nests on land

    ○   the riv·**er**

    ○   up in trees

3. What p**ar**t helps riv·**er** ott·**er**s swim fast?

    ○   webbed paws

    ○   point·ed nose

    ○   sh**ar**p claws

Directions: Have students reread the story and answer the questions.

4. What do riv·**er** ott·**er**s like f**or** food?

_____

- -

_____

- -

_____

_____

- -

_____

_____

- -

_____

Name of Critt·er: _____

I will des·cribe: _____
_____

What it looks like: _____
_____
_____

What it sounds like: _____

_____

_____

What it feels like: _____

_____

_____

Where is its home? _____

_____

_____

What food would it like? _____

_____

_____

Name _____

Name of Critt·er: _____

I will des·cribe: _____

_____

What it looks like: _____

_____

Directions: Have students respond to the prompts, using the Reader as a resource.

What it sounds like: _____

_____

_____

_____

What it feels like: _____

_____

_____

_____

Where is its home? _____

_____

_____

_____

What food would it like? _____

_____

_____

_____

Name of Critt·er: _____

I will des·cribe: _____

_____

_____

What it looks like: _____

_____

_____

_____

What it sounds like: _____

_____

What it feels like: _____

_____

Where is its home? _____

_____

What food would it like? _____

_____

What it sounds like: _____

_____

- -

_____

- -

_____

What it feels like: _____

_____

- -

_____

- -

_____

Where is its home? _____

_____

- -

_____

- -

_____

What food would it like? _____

_____

- -

_____

- -

_____

Name of Critt·er: _____

I will des·cribe: _____

_____

What it looks like: _____

_____

_____

Name of Critt·er: _____
_____

I will des·cribe: _____
_____
_____

What it looks like: _____
_____
_____
_____
_____

Directions: Have students respond to the prompts, using the Reader as a resource.

What it sounds like: _____

_____

_____

What it feels like: _____

_____

_____

Where is its home? _____

_____

_____

What food would it like? _____

_____

_____

Name of Critt·er: _____

I will des·cribe: _____

_____

_____

What it looks like: _____

_____

_____

_____

Directions: Have students respond to the prompts, using the Reader as a resource.

What it sounds like: _____

_____

_____

What it feels like: _____

_____

_____

Where is its home? _____

_____

_____

What food would it like? _____

_____

_____

_____

Name of Critt·er: _____

_____

I will des·cribe: _____

_____

_____

What it looks like: _____

_____

_____

_____

What it sounds like: _____

_____

_____

What it feels like: _____

_____

_____

Where is its home? _____

_____

_____

What food would it like? _____

_____

_____

1. Yes·**ter**·d<u>ay</u> the dog _____ the food on the **car**·pet.
(lick)

2. My pal _____ at us.
(grin)

3. Fran lost h**er** tem·p**er** and

_____.
(yell)

4. She _____ wood in h**er** back·y**ar**d.
(chop)

5. I _____ a cake yes·**ter**·d<u>ay</u> f**or** my class.
(bake)

Dear Family Member,

   This is a story your child has probably read once, possibly several times, at school. Encourage your child to read the story to you and then talk about it together. The tricky parts in Tricky Words are underlined in gray. Please note that the multi-syllable words are divided between syllables with a dot. This dot serves as a cue to assist students in chunking syllables, and will be omitted in later units.

   Repeated oral reading is an important way to improve reading skills. It can be fun for your child to repeatedly read this story to a friend, relative, or even a pet.

Big Cats

   Do you like cats? If you do, look there in the grass. Do you see the cat?

   That is not the **so**rt of cat that you keep in your home and feed cat food. That is a bob·cat.

   Bob·cats are good hunt·**er**s. They hunt rabb·its, rats, and some·times deer and sheep.

   That bob·cat's name is Rob·**er**t, **or** Bob f**or** sh**or**t. Get it?

If you look up on that rock, you will see a cat that's bigg·**er** than a bob·cat. It's a pan·th**er**.

Pan·th**er**s can have spots. They can be tan, too. Here at the Green F**er**n Zoo, we have t<u>wo</u> black pan·th**er**s. The name of this one is Jet.

That's Jet's sis·t**er**, Flash, up on the tree branch. Flash has strong legs that help h**er** run fast. She has sh**ar**p teeth and sh**ar**p claws that help h**er** hunt rabb·its and deer. She can use h**er** claws to scam·p**er** up a tree if she needs to.

You can see that she is not all black like Jet. She has s<u>ome</u> spots.

Name of Critter:

_____

- -

_____

_____

- -

I will des·cribe _____

_____

- -

_____

- -

Des·cribe what it looks like, sounds like, and feels like:

_____

- -

_____

_____

- -

_____

_____

_____

- -

_____

_____

- -

_____

Home:

Food:

Fun Fact:

End:

Name _____

Dear Family Member,

Your child has been learning about nouns and verbs. The dot in words shows that this is a two-syllable word. Please have your child read the sentences, then circle the nouns and underline the verbs with a squiggly line. You may ask your child to act out the action.

1. The dog b**ar**ks.

2. To·d<u>ay</u> my sis·**ter** will take a nap.

3. To·morr·<u>ow</u> the kid will sing a song.

4. Yes·**ter**·d<u>ay</u> the cat licked h**er** paws.

5. To·morr·<u>ow</u> Gran will bake a cake.

6. To·d<u>ay</u> the man point·ed to the clouds.

7. Yes·**ter**·d<u>ay</u> my pal took a trip.

8. To·d<u>ay</u> the sh**ar**k swims.

9. The kid grinned at us.

10. Yes·**ter**·d<u>ay</u> the ground·hog was stuffed with food.

Check the Draft Step by Step

Name of Part·ner: _____

Ed·it·ed by: _____

Step	Check?
Check that the name of the critt·**er** is there.	
Check that you des·cribed what it looks like.	
Check that you des·cribed its home.	
Check that you des·cribed its food.	
Check that you list·ed a fun fact.	
Aa, Bb, Cc and ? . !	
Check that the words are spelled well.	

Dear Family Member,

Your child has been learning about compound words. Please have your child read the compound words in the box and place them in the correct sentence. Your child will practice making up their own silly compound words on the back of the worksheet.

| bath·tub   pop·corn   gum·drop |
| back·pack   lunch·box |

1. My snack is in my _____.

2. I like _____ **for** a snack.

3. This _____ is sweet!

4. I take a bath in the _____.

5. The book is in my _____.

+ = dogcake

1. ☐ + ☐ =

2. ☐ + ☐ =

3. ☐ + ☐ =

4. ☐ + ☐ =

Part I

1. The dog b**ar**ks.

2. To·d<u>ay</u> the sh**ar**k swims.

3. To·m<u>orr</u>·<u>ow</u> the kid will sing.

4. Yes·**ter**·d<u>ay</u> the cat walked.

5. To·m<u>orr</u>·<u>ow</u> Gran will bake.

Part II

it is   there's

there is   she's

let us   it's

here is   let's

she is   here's

Directions: Have students circle the noun and underline the verb with a squiggly line. In Part II, have students match the words with its contraction. In Part III, have students write the past-tense form of the verbs.

Part III

To·d<u>ay</u> I bake.

Yes·**ter**·d<u>ay</u> I _____ .

To·m<u>orr</u>·<u>ow</u> I will _____ .

To·d<u>ay</u> you smile.

Yes·**ter**·d<u>ay</u> you _____ .

To·m<u>orr</u>·<u>ow</u> you will _____ .

To·d<u>ay</u> I hike.

Yes·**ter**·d<u>ay</u> I _____ .

To·m<u>orr</u>·<u>ow</u> I will _____ .

To·d<u>ay</u> she points.

Yes·**ter**·d<u>ay</u> she _____ .

To·m<u>orr</u>·<u>ow</u> she will _____ .

Amber the Bat

This is Am·b**er**. Am·b**er** looks a bit like a fox. But she has wings and swings from trees. In fact, Am·b**er** is a bat.

Am·b**er** needs a lot of room to glide back and f**or**th be·<u>ca</u><u>u</u>se she has a wing·span of five feet. In fact, bats like Am·b**er** are the bigg·est bats there are!

Am·b**er** makes h**er** home here at Green F**er**n Zoo. She has all the room she needs at the zoo. <u>S</u><u>o</u>m<u>e</u> bats like Am·b**er** make their homes in the trop·ics, <u>where</u> the sun shines and it is hot.

Directions: Have students read the story and answer the questions on the following pages.

Bats like Am·b**er** feed on plant p**ar**ts and poll·en. They can smell lots of things, so they use th<u>ei</u>r nose to look f**or** food. They use th<u>ei</u>r wings to glide from plant to plant to gath·**er** th<u>ei</u>r food. In fact, they can trav·el up to 40 miles to gath·**er** food!

Look at Am·b**er** here in the tree. Am·b**er** likes to do things up·side d<u>ow</u>n. She hangs out up·side d<u>ow</u>n. She sleeps up·side d<u>ow</u>n. When she has food, she clings to the branch with h**er** feet and will munch on h**er** food up·side d<u>ow</u>n! What can you do up·side d<u>ow</u>n?

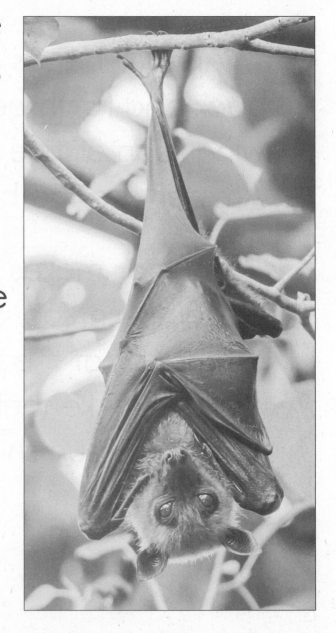

1. **What is Am·b*er*?**

   ○ a fox

   ○ a bat

   ○ a dog

   ○ a cat

2. **Am·b*er*'s wings are _____ long.**

   ○ three feet

   ○ three wing·spans

   ○ t<u>wo</u> feet

   ○ five feet

Directions: Have students use the story on the previous pages to answer the questions.

3. <u>Where</u> do bats like Am·b**er** make th**eir** homes?

   ○ up in the n**or**th

   ○ in the trop·ics

   ○ in the des·**er**t

   ○ in cool lakes

4. What do bats like Am·b**er** feed on?

   ○ fish

   ○ grubs and slugs

   ○ milk

   ○ plant p**ar**ts and poll·en

5. What p**ar**t do bats like Am·b**er** use to look f**or** food?

   ○ nose

   ○ legs

   ○ teeth

   ○ fins

6. Bats like Am·b**er** can trav·el . . .

   ○ up to 10 miles to gath·**er** food

   ○ up to 40 miles to gath·**er** food

   ○ as far as three miles to gath·**er** food

   ○ as far as five feet to gath·**er** food

7. What things can Am·b**er** do up·side <u>down</u>?

   ○ sing a sweet song, sleep, and munch on food

   ○ hang out, trav·el, and sleep

   ○ hang out, sleep, and munch on food

   ○ just munch on food

8. It says, "Am·b**er** needs a lot of room to glide back and f**or**th . . ."

    Glide is a word f**or**:

    ○ swim

    ○ trav·el

    ○ hop

    ○ sleep

9. <u>Why</u> would Am·b**er** need a lot of room to glide back and f**or**th?

    ○ <u>be</u>·<u>cause</u> there are lots of bats at the zoo

    ○ <u>be</u>·<u>cause</u> she is one of the bigg·est bats there are

    ○ <u>be</u>·<u>cause</u> there are lots of in·sects at the zoo

    ○ <u>be</u>·<u>cause</u> there are trees at the zoo

Directions: Have students trace and copy the digraphs and words. Students should say the sounds while writing the letters.

er   ar

er   ar

herd   herd

ar   ar

ar   ar

barn   barn

or   or

or   or

corn   corn

er

er

herd

ar

ar

barn

or

or

corn

Count the sounds in the words. Print the num·**ber** of sounds in the box·es and print the words on the lines.

1. hamm·**er** | 4 | hammer

2. b**or**n | | _____

3. b**ar**ns | | _____

4. d**ar**k·**er** | | _____

5. cool·**er** | | _____

6. pepp·**er** | | _____

7. riv·**er** | | _____

8. sh**ar**ks | | _____

9. h**or**ns

10. blis·t**er**

11. cook**ed**

12. c**ar**·pet

13. chill**ed**

14. lett·**er**

15. sn**or**·ing

16. g**ar**·lic

her /er/	barn /ar/
hard / /	bett·er / /
car·pet / /	lan·tern / /
herd / /	arm / /
dark·ness / /	per·fect / /

/er/   **/ar/**

her   barn

Directions: Have students write the /r/-controlled vowel sound in each word in the slashes. Then have students write the words with the /er/ sound under the /er/ header and the words with the /ar/ sound under the /ar/ header.

barn /ar/			**horn** /or/	
p**ar**ked / /			f**or**ks / /	
y**ar**d / /			pop·c**or**n / /	
f**or**med / /			g**ar**·den / /	
h**ar**·vest / /			t**or**ch / /	

/ar/

barn

/or/

horn

Directions: Have students cut out the word cards and place them on the matching words on Worksheet PP5.

c**ou**ld	ask**ed**	num·b**er**
h**ar**d	st**art**·ed	seem**ed**
sh**or**t	h**or**n	t**wo**
lik**ed**	spell**ed**	runn·**er**s
p**o**rch	c**a**rs	help**ed**

Directions: Have students read the word cards from Worksheet PP4 and place them on top of the matching words on this worksheet.

two	horn	short
could	num·b**er**	ask**ed**
st**art**·ed	h**ar**d	lik**ed**
p**o**rch	spell**ed**	runn·**er**s
c**ar**s	help**ed**	seem**ed**

Mark the words that are said and print them on the lines.

1. short·en   short·er   _____

2. gar·den   gar·lic   _____

3. snor·ing   snarl·ing   _____

4. hor·net   hors·es   _____

5. mar·ket   mark·er   _____

6. bett·er   bitt·er   _____

7. for·tress   for·est   _____

8. har·vest   harm·less   _____

9. bor·der   bar·ter   _____

10. sharp·er   smart·er   _____

Print the words.

barn

yard

sharp

dark

arm

Print the words.

barn

yard

sharp

dark

arm

Print the words.

horn

sport

north

short

thorn

Print the words.

horn

sport

north

short

thorn

Print the words.

herd

herd

perk

perk

fern

fern

verb

verb

perch

perch

Print the words.

herd

perk

fern

verb

perch

Print the words on the lines where they fit best.

1. sh**ar**k

2. hamm·**er**

3. h**or**·net

4. zipp·**er**

5. st**or**k

In the box are six words. Print them on the lines where they fit best.

shark	fork	hang·er
scarf	cake	horn

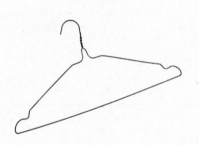

_____

- - - - - - - - - - - - -

_____

_____

- - - - - - - - - - - - -

_____

In the box are six words. Print them on the lines where they fit best.

hor·net   ham·ster   hawk

gar·lic   cloud   pop·corn

_____

- - - - - - - - -

_____

_____

- - - - - - - - -

_____

Directions: Have students copy the word onto the left side of the paper, fold it in half, and then write the word from memory on the right side of the paper.

1. _____

2. _____

3. _____

4. _____

5. _____

6. _____

7. _____

8. _____

9. _____

10. _____

1. _____

2. _____

3. _____

4. _____

5. _____

6. _____

7. _____

8. _____

9. _____

10. _____

Print the words.

today   today

yesterday   yesterday

tomorrow   tomorrow

to   to

too   too

two   two

here   here

there   there

said   said

says   says

Print the words.

today

yesterday

tomorrow

to

too

two

here

there

said

says

Mark the words that are said.

1. big st**or**m | big step

2. af·t**er** class | af·t**er** d**ar**k

3. strong legs | strong **ar**ms

4. c<u>ou</u>ld not run | sh<u>ou</u>ld not run

5. boil**ed** eggs | soft eggs

6. a red c**ar**·pet | a red c**ar**

7. coil**ed** up snake | coil**ed** up rope

8. plant a g**ar**·den | keep a g**ar**·den

9. use a f**or**k | use a broom

10. f**ar**·th**er** n**or**th | f**ar**·th**er** south

Fill in the _____ with the words that are in the box.

~~out·side~~	sing·ing
b**ark**·ing	**car**·pet
book·case	f**or**·est

1. Jen went ⸱⸱⸱outside⸱⸱⸱ to the y**ar**d.

2. Kate set the books on the
   _____
   ─ ─ ─ ─ ─ ─ ─ ─
   _____ .

3. Brent was _____ a song.

4. There are lots of trees in a
   _____
   ─ ─ ─ ─ ─ ─ ─ ─
   _____ .

5. The dog was _____ all m**or**n·ing.

6. There is a red _____ in this room.

Fill in the _____ with the words that are in the box.

fast·**er**	jump·ing
ant·**ler**s	lunch·time
tem·p**er**	tool·box

1. Ben likes _____ on the bed.

2. Dad got his _____ so he

   could fix the pipe.

3. Trish is fast, but Beth is _____ .

4. Mom lost h**er** _____

   and yell**ed** at the dog.

5. The deer has sh**ar**p _____ .

6. Is it _____ yet?

Fill in the _____ with the words that are in the box.

blis·ters	park·ing
matt·ress	licked
sand·wich	Fire·men

1. Af·ter the hike I had _blisters_ on my feet.

   _____

2. Fran ate her _____.

   _____

3. Dad found a _____ spot for the car.

   _____

4. _____ ride on a red truck.

   _____

5. I have a soft _____ on my bed.

   _____

6. The man was _____ by a dog.

Fill in the _____ with the words that are in the box.

melt·ed	muff·ins
pop·**corn**	nos·trils
art·ist	sev·en

1. The flame _____ the wax.

2. Can you bake _____ f**or** me?

3. An _____ makes **ar**t.

4. Af·t**er** six we count to _____.

5. Is it fun to pop _____?

6. Your nose has two _____.

Yes or no? Print *yes* **or** *no* on the lines.

1. Do kids have a
   bed·time?   _____

2. Are your bones soft?   _____

3. Do **ar**t·ists use brush·es? _____

4. Can a back·yard have
   grass?   _____

5. Should you make a
   camp·fire in·side?   _____

6. Can chil·dren drive
   cars?   _____

7. Do kitt·ens have teeth?   _____

8. Could a plant sip a
   milk·shake?   _____

Yes or no? Print *yes* **or** *no* on the lines.

1. Should you drop trash on the ground?

_____

2. Do some parks have slides?

_____

3. Can you bake a cake in a round pan?

_____

4. Is a trip to the den·tist fun?

_____

5. Can you hike out·side in the summ·**er**?

_____

6. Would a pet fish like to sleep in a bed?

_____

7. Are pig·lets cute?

_____

8. Is sev·en a num·b**er**?

_____

Dear Family Member,

    This is a story your child has probably read once, possibly several times, at school. Encourage your child to read the story to you and then talk about it together. The tricky parts in Tricky Words are underlined in gray. Please note that the multi-syllable words are divided between syllables with a dot. This dot serves as a cue to assist students in chunking syllables, and will be omitted in later units.

    Repeated oral reading is an important way to improve reading skills. It can be fun for your child to repeatedly read this story to a friend, relative, or even a pet.

Mandrills

Here you can see t<u>wo</u> man·drills. Man·drills are a lot like chimps.

D<u>o</u> you like the red nose? The man·drill with the red nose is a male.

The man·drill on the left is groom·ing the male with the red nose. She is look·ing **for** ticks and bugs. Man·drills like groom·ing be·c<u>au</u>se it makes them look good and feel good, too.

Look! One of the man·drills is yawn·ing! You can see that he has long, sh**ar**p teeth. Those sh**ar**p teeth help him chop up his food.

Man·drills like a lot of foods. We feed our man·drills ants, grass, nuts, b**ar**k, plant shoots, and roots.

Man·drills have sacks in·side of th<u>ei</u>r cheeks. They can stuff food in the sacks and keep it there un·til they need a snack. Then they pop the food out and munch on it!

Dear Family Member,

This is a story your child has probably read once, possibly several times, at school. Encourage your child to read the story to you and then talk about it together. The tricky parts in Tricky Words are underlined in gray. Please note that the multi-syllable words are divided between syllables with a dot. This dot serves as a cue to assist students in chunking syllables, and will be omitted in later units.

Repeated oral reading is an important way to improve reading skills. It can be fun for your child to repeatedly read this story to a friend, relative, or even a pet.

Groundhogs

Here you can see a ground·hog.

Ground·hogs have sh**ar**p claws that help them dig holes in the ground. They spend a lot of time d**ow**n in those d**ar**k holes.

Ground·hogs like to feed on grass and plants. But when they run out of th**eir** holes to get food, they have to be on the look·out. S**ome** critt·**er**s, like bob·cats and snakes, like to dine on ground·hogs. This ground·hog here is sitt·ing up to see if there is a snake **or** a bob·cat close by.

This ground·hog is named Pepp·**er**. We f**ee**d h**er** grass, tree b**ar**k, and in·sects, but the food that she likes best is c**or**n. We found that out yes·t**er**·d<u>ay</u> m**or**n·ing when she got out fr<u>o</u>m h**er** pen.

We found h**er** in the pett·ing zoo. She ate a lot of the c**or**n that was there f**or** the ducks and hens.

Dear Family Member,

This is a story your child has probably read once, possibly several times, at school. Encourage your child to read the story to you and then talk about it together. The tricky parts in Tricky Words are underlined in gray. Please note that the multi-syllable words are divided between syllables with a dot. This dot serves as a cue to assist students in chunking syllables, and will be omitted in later units.

Repeated oral reading is an important way to improve reading skills. It can be fun for your child to repeatedly read this story to a friend, relative, or even a pet.

Termites

What do you kids like to have f**or** lunch? Hot dogs? Chick·en nugg·ets?

What if I gave you a lump of wood **or** a big tree stump f**or** lunch? W<u>ou</u>ld you like that?

Well, if you were a **ter**·mite, you w<u>ou</u>ld like it. **Ter**·mites are in·sects that like to munch on wood.

See this big spike stick·ing up from the ground? It looks s**or**t of like a rock, but it is a **ter**·mite mound. If you c<u>ou</u>ld look in·side, you w<u>ou</u>ld see lots of **ter**·mites.

If you would like to see what **ter**·mites look like, take a peek in this box.

As you can see, **ter**·mites look a lot like ants. They have six legs like ants. A **ter**·mite mound has a queen who makes eggs, just like in an ant·hill. Here you can see that the **ter**·mite queen is much bigg·**er** than the rest of the **ter**·mites.

Would a **ter**·mite munch on your home? It would if your home is made of wood. The **ter**·mites from a big mound could have your liv·ing room f**or** lunch and your bed·room f**or** dinn·**er**!

Name _____

The Ostrich

1. The os·trich at the Green **Fer**n Zoo tips the scales at…

   ○ three hun·dred pounds.

   ○ two pounds.

   ○ two hun·dred pounds.

2. Can an os·trich run fast?

   _____

   -

   _____

   -

   _____

   -

   _____

   -

   _____

Directions: Have students reread the story and answer the questions.

Directions: Have students write about the animal in the picture or copy their favorite sentences from the story that tell something about the animal.

_____

- -

_____

- -

_____

- -

_____

- -

_____

- -

_____

166 *Unit 4*

Deer

1. Was Hope b**or**n in the zoo?

_____

- - - - - - - - - - - - - - - - -

_____

- - - - - - - - - - - - - - - - -

_____

2. What happ·en**ed** to Hope's leg?

_____

- - - - - - - - - - - - - - - - -

_____

- - - - - - - - - - - - - - - - -

_____

- - - - - - - - - - - - - - - - -

_____

Directions: Have students reread the story and answer the questions.

Directions: Have students write about the animal in the picture or copy their favorite sentences from the story that tell something about the animal.

The Petting Zoo

1. What is the rabb·it's name?

_____
- -
_____
- -
_____
- -
_____

2. What scares the chick·ens?

_____
- -
_____
- -
_____
- -
_____
- -
_____
- -
_____

Directions: Have students reread the story and answer the questions.

3. <u>Which</u> critt·**er** from the pett·ing zoo do you like best? <u>Why?</u>

Cut out the cards.

- -

- -

- -

Directions: Have students underline the past-tense marker 'ed' in each word. Then have the student write the final sound(s) in each word in the slashes. Then have the student write the past-tense verbs that end in /ed/ under the /ed/ header, the verbs that end in /d/ under the /d/ header, and the verbs that end in /t/ under the /t/ header.

start·**ed** /ed/	grinn**ed** /d/	help**ed** /t/	nodd·**ed** / /	horn**ed** / /	mark**ed** / /
plant·ed / /	snarl**ed** / /	smok**ed** / /	greet·**ed** / /	doz**ed** / /	shap**ed** / /

/t/

/d/

/ed/

CORE KNOWLEDGE LANGUAGE ARTS

SERIES EDITOR-IN-CHIEF
E. D. Hirsch, Jr.

PRESIDENT
Linda Bevilacqua

EDITORIAL STAFF
Carolyn Gosse, Senior Editor - Preschool
Khara Turnbull, Materials Development Manager
Michelle L. Warner, Senior Editor - Listening & Learning

Mick Anderson
Robin Blackshire
Maggie Buchanan
Paula Coyner
Sue Fulton
Sara Hunt
Erin Kist
Robin Luecke
Rosie McCormick
Cynthia Peng
Liz Pettit
Ellen Sadler
Deborah Samley
Diane Auger Smith
Sarah Zelinke

DESIGN AND GRAPHICS STAFF
Scott Ritchie, Creative Director

Kim Berrall
Michael Donegan
Liza Greene
Matt Leech
Bridget Moriarty
Lauren Pack

CONSULTING PROJECT MANAGEMENT SERVICES
ScribeConcepts.com

ADDITIONAL CONSULTING SERVICES
Ang Blanchette
Dorrit Green
Carolyn Pinkerton

ACKNOWLEDGMENTS

These materials are the result of the work, advice, and encouragement of numerous individuals over many years. Some of those singled out here already know the depth of our gratitude; others may be surprised to find themselves thanked publicly for help they gave quietly and generously for the sake of the enterprise alone. To helpers named and unnamed we are deeply grateful.

CONTRIBUTORS TO EARLIER VERSIONS OF THESE MATERIALS

Susan B. Albaugh, Kazuko Ashizawa, Nancy Braier, Kathryn M. Cummings, Michelle De Groot, Diana Espinal, Mary E. Forbes, Michael L. Ford, Ted Hirsch, Danielle Knecht, James K. Lee, Diane Henry Leipzig, Martha G. Mack, Liana Mahoney, Isabel McLean, Steve Morrison, Juliane K. Munson, Elizabeth B. Rasmussen, Laura Tortorelli, Rachael L. Shaw, Sivan B. Sherman, Miriam E. Vidaver, Catherine S. Whittington, Jeannette A. Williams

We would like to extend special recognition to Program Directors Matthew Davis and Souzanne Wright who were instrumental to the early development of this program.

SCHOOLS

We are truly grateful to the teachers, students, and administrators of the following schools for their willingness to field test these materials and for their invaluable advice: Capitol View Elementary, Challenge Foundation Academy (IN), Community Academy Public Charter School, Lake Lure Classical Academy, Lepanto Elementary School, New Holland Core Knowledge Academy, Paramount School of Excellence, Pioneer Challenge Foundation Academy, New York City PS 26R (The Carteret School), PS 30X (Wilton School), PS 50X (Clara Barton School), PS 96Q, PS 102X (Joseph O. Loretan), PS 104Q (The Bays Water), PS 214K (Michael Friedsam), PS 223Q (Lyndon B. Johnson School), PS 308K (Clara Cardwell), PS 333Q (Goldie Maple Academy), Sequoyah Elementary School, South Shore Charter Public School, Spartanburg Charter School, Steed Elementary School, Thomas Jefferson Classical Academy, Three Oaks Elementary, West Manor Elementary.

And a special thanks to the CKLA Pilot Coordinators Anita Henderson, Yasmin Lugo-Hernandez, and Susan Smith, whose suggestions and day-to-day support to teachers using these materials in their classrooms was critical.

CREDITS

ILLUSTRATORS AND IMAGE SOURCES

Cover: Shutterstock; Title Page: Shutterstock; Take Home Icon: Core Knowledge Staff; 1.2: Shutterstock; 4.1: Shutterstock; 5.3 : Shutterstock; 5.3 (Vern): Michael Parker; 7.1: Shutterstock; 8.2: Shutterstock; 10.3: Shutterstock; 12.3: Shutterstock; 17.2: Shutterstock; 18.1: Shutterstock; 20.2: Shutterstock; 22.1: Shutterstock; 22.2: Shutterstock; 22.3: Shutterstock; 22.4: Shutterstock; 22.5: Shutterstock; 22.6: Shutterstock; 22.8: Shutterstock; 24.2: Shutterstock; 26.1: Shutterstock; PP10: Shutterstock; PP11: Shutterstock; PP18: Shutterstock; PP19: Shutterstock; PP20: Shutterstock; PP21: Shutterstock; PP22: Shutterstock; PP24: Shutterstock

PROBLEM 9-4A or 9-4B

PAYROLL REGISTER

	NAME	TOTAL HOURS	BEGINNING CUMULATIVE EARNINGS	TOTAL EARNINGS	ENDING CUMULATIVE EARNINGS	TAXABLE EARNIN	
						UNEMPLOYMENT	SOCIAL SECURITY
1	Bach, C. E.	44	22 95 00 00				
2	Ball, V. A.	40	27 41 00 00				
3	Church, J. P.	40	26 86 00 00				
4	Entzel, N. D.	44	22 49 00 00				
5	Gram, J. W.	48	26 98 00 00				
6	King, D. C.	40	53 55 00 00				
7	Magana, R. G.	40	26 86 00 00				
8	Moody, P. M.	40	26 75 00 00				
9	Olson, T. B.	44	23 48 00 00				
10	Ross, K. C.	42	41 00 00 00				
11							
12							
13							
14							
15							
16							
17							
18							
19							
20							
21							
22							
23							
24							
25							
26							
27							
28							
29							
30							
31							
32							
33							
34							
35							

NGS		DEDUCTIONS					PAYMENTS		
	MEDICARE	FEDERAL INCOME TAX	SOCIAL SECURITY TAX	MEDICARE TAX		TOTAL	NET AMOUNT	CK. NO.	WAGES EXPENSE DEBIT
										1
										2
										3
										4
										5
										6
										7
										8
										9
										10
										11
										12
										13
										14
										15
										16
										17
										18
										19
										20
										21
										22
										23
										24
										25
										26
										27
										28
										29
										30
										31
										32
										33
										34
										35

A-17

PROBLEM 9-2A or 9-2B

PAYROLL REGISTER F◗

	NAME	TOTAL HOURS	BEGINNING CUMULATIVE EARNINGS	EARNINGS			ENDING CUMULATIVE EARNINGS	
				REGULAR	OVERTIME	TOTAL		ﾚ
1								
2								
3								
4								
5								
6								
7								
8								
9								
10								
11								
12								
13								
14								
15								
16								
17								
18								
19								
20								
21								
22								
23								
24								
25								
26								
27								
28								
29								
30								
31								
32								
33								
34								
35								

					1
					2
					3
					4
					5
					6
					7
					8
					9
					10
					11
					12
					13
					14
					15
					16
					17
					18
					19
					20
					21
					22
					23
					24
					25
					26
					27
					28
					29
					30
					31
					32
					33
					34
					35
					36
					37
					38

PROBLEM 7-3A or 7-3B

COMBINE

	CASH		CK. NO.	DATE	ACCOUNT NAME	POST. REF.	OTHER ACC	
	DEBIT	CREDIT					DEBIT	
1								
2								
3								
4								
5								
6								
7								
8								
9								
10								
11								
12								
13								
14								
15								
16								
17								
18								
19								
20								
21								
22								
23								
24								
25								
26								
27								
28								
29								
30								
31								
32								
33								
34								
35								
36								
37								

SUPPLIES	DRAWING	ADVERTISING EXPENSE	PROFESSIONAL FEES	TRAVEL EXPENSE	MISCELLANEOUS EXPENSE	
DEBIT	DEBIT	DEBIT	CREDIT	DEBIT	DEBIT	
						1
						2
						3
						4
						5
						6
						7
						8
						9
						10
						11
						12
						13
						14
						15
						16
						17
						18
						19
						20
						21
						22
						23
						24
						25
						26
						27
						28
						29
						30
						31
						32
						33
						34
						35

PROBLEM 7-1A or 7-1B

	CASH		CK. NO.	DATE	ACCOUNT NAME	POST. REF.	OTHER ACC	
	DEBIT	CREDIT					DEBIT	
1								
2								
3								
4								
5								
6								
7								
8								
9								
10								
11								
12								
13								
14								
15								
16								
17								
18								
19								
20								
21								
22								
23								
24								
25								
26								
27								
28								
29								
30								
31								
32								
33								
34								
35								

ADJUSTED TRIAL BALANCE		INCOME STATEMENT		BALANCE SHEET	
DEBIT	CREDIT	DEBIT	CREDIT	DEBIT	CREDIT
						1
						2
						3
						4
						5
						6
						7
						8
						9
						10
						11
						12
						13
						14
						15
						16
						17
						18
						19
						20
						21
						22
						23
						24
						25
						26
						27
						28
						29
						30
						31
						32
						33
						34

ACCOUNTING CYCLE REVIEW PROBLEM

Fun World W

Work S

For Month Ended

	ACCOUNT NAME	TRIAL BALANCE		ADJUSTMENTS	
		DEBIT	CREDIT	DEBIT	CREDIT
1	Cash				
2	Accounts Receivable				
3	Supplies				
4	Prepaid Insurance				
5	Land				
6	Building				
7	Pool/Slide Facility				
8	Pool Furniture				
9	Accounts Payable				
10	Mortgage Payable				
11	K. Taylor, Capital				
12	K. Taylor, Drawing				
13	Income from Services				
14	Concession Income				
15	Pool Maintenance Expense				
16	Wages Expense				
17	Advertising Expense				
18	Utilities Expense				
19	Interest Expense				
20	Miscellaneous Expense				
21					
22	Insurance Expense				
23	Depreciation Expense, Building				
24	Accum. Depreciation, Building				
25	Deprec. Expense, Pool/Slide Facility				
26	Accum. Depreciation, Pool/Slide				
27	Facility				
28	Depreciation Expense, Pool Furniture				
29	Accum. Depreciation, Pool Furniture				
30	Wages Payable				
31	Supplies Expense				
32					
33	Net Income				
34					

	MEDICAL SUPPLIES	DRAWING	PROFESSIONAL FEES	LABORATORY EXPENSE	CLEANING EXPENSE	MISCELLANEOUS EXPENSE	
T	DEBIT	DEBIT	CREDIT	DEBIT	DEBIT	DEBIT	
							1
							2
							3
							4
							5
							6
							7
							8
							9
							10
							11
							12
							13
							14
							15
							16
							17
							18
							19
							20
							21
							22
							23
							24
							25
							26
							27
							28
							29
							30
							31
							32
							33
							34
							35

PROBLEM 7-2A or 7-2B

COMBINED

	CASH		CK. NO.	DATE	ACCOUNT NAME	POST. REF.	OTHER ACCOUNTS	
	DEBIT	CREDIT					DEBIT	CREDIT
1								
2								
3								
4								
5								
6								
7								
8								
9								
10								
11								
12								
13								
14								
15								
16								
17								
18								
19								
20								
21								
22								
23								
24								
25								
26								
27								
28								
29								
30								
31								
32								
33								
34								
35								

	ACCOUNTS RECEIVABLE		PROFESSIONAL FEES	SALARY EXPENSE	UTILITIES EXPENSE	
	DEBIT	CREDIT	CREDIT	DEBIT	DEBIT	
						1
						2
						3
						4
						5
						6
						7
						8
						9
						10
						11
						12
						13
						14
						15
						16
						17
						18
						19
						20
						21
						22
						23
						24
						25
						26
						27
						28
						29
						30
						31
						32
						33
						34
						35
						36
						37

PROBLEM 7-4A or 7-4B

1									
2									
3									
4									
5									
6									
7									
8									
9									
10									
11									
12									
13									
14									
15									
16									
17									
18									
19									
20									
21									
22									
23									
24									
25									
26									
27									
28									
29									
30									
31									
32									
33									
34									
35									
36									
37									
38									

| TAXABLE EARNINGS | | DEDUCTIONS | | | | PAYMENTS | | WAGES EXPENSE DEBIT | |
SOCIAL SECURITY	MEDICARE	FEDERAL INCOME TAX	SOCIAL SECURITY TAX	MEDICARE TAX	TOTAL	NET AMOUNT	CK. NO.	WAGES EXPENSE DEBIT	
									1
									2
									3
									4
									5
									6
									7
									8
									9
									10
									11
									12
									13
									14
									15
									16
									17
									18
									19
									20
									21
									22
									23
									24
									25
									26
									27
									28
									29
									30
									31
									32
									33
									34
									35

PROBLEM 9-3A or 9-3B

PAYROLL REGISTER FOR WEEK E

	NAME	TOTAL HOURS	BEGINNING CUMULATIVE EARNINGS	EARNINGS			ENDING CUMULATIVE EARNINGS	T
				REGULAR	OVERTIME	TOTAL		UNEMPLOYMENT
1								
2								
3								
4								
5								
6								
7								
8								
9								
10								
11								
12								
13								
14								
15								
16								
17								
18								
19								
20								
21								
22								
23								
24								
25								
26								
27								
28								
29								
30								
31								
32								
33								
34								
35								

		DEDUCTIONS							PAYMENTS		EXPENSE ACCOUNT DEBITED		
RE		FEDERAL INCOME TAX	SOCIAL SECURITY TAX	MEDICARE TAX	OTHER		TOTAL		NET AMOUNT	CK. NO.	SALES SALARY EXPENSE	OFFICE SALARY EXPENSE	
					CODE	AMOUNT							
													1
													2
													3
													4
													5
													6
													7
													8
													9
													10
													11
													12
													13
													14
													15
													16
													17
													18
													19
													20
													21
													22
													23
													24
													25
													26
													27
													28
													29
													30
													31
													32
													33
													34
													35

COMPREHENSIVE REVIEW PROBLEM

_____

_____

_____ *For Mon*

	ACCOUNT NAME	TRIAL B.
		DEBIT
1	Cash	
2	Petty Cash Fund	
3	Accounts Receivable	
4	Merchandise Inventory	
5	Supplies	
6	Prepaid Insurance	
7	Equipment	
8	Accumulated Depreciation, Equipment	
9	Accounts Payable	
10	Employees' Income Tax Payable	
11	FICA Tax Payable	
12	State Unemployment Tax Payable	
13	Federal Unemployment Tax Payable	
14	N. R. Bell, Capital	
15	N. R. Bell, Drawing	
16	Sales	
17	Sales Returns and Allowances	
18	Purchases	
19	Purchases Returns and Allowances	
20	Purchases Discount	
21	Freight In	
22	Salary Expense	
23	Payroll Tax Expense	
24	Rent Expense	
25	Utilities Expense	
26	Miscellaneous Expense	
27		
28		
29		
30		
31		
32		
33		
34		
35		

January 15, 19—

DEDUCTIONS					PAYMENTS		SALARY EXPENSE	
INCOME TAX	SOCIAL SECURITY TAX	MEDICARE TAX		TOTAL	NET AMOUNT	CK. NO.	DEBIT	
382 20	169 26		39 59	591 05	2138 95	7154	2730 00	1
313 60	138 88		32 48	484 96	1755 04	7155	2240 00	2
695 80	308 14		72 07	1076 01	3893 99		4970 00	3
								4

January 29, 19—

DEDUCTIONS					PAYMENTS		SALARY EXPENSE	
INCOME TAX	SOCIAL SECURITY TAX	MEDICARE TAX		TOTAL	NET AMOUNT	CK. NO.	DEBIT	
382 20	169 26		39 59	591 05	2138 95	7182	2730 00	1
313 60	138 88		32 48	484 96	1755 04	7183	2240 00	2
695 80	308 14		72 07	1076 01	3893 99		4970 00	3
								4

DEDUCTIONS					PAYMENTS		SALARY EXPENSE	
INCOME TAX	SOCIAL SECURITY TAX	MEDICARE TAX		TOTAL	NET AMOUNT	CK. NO.	DEBIT	
								1
								2
								3
								4

DEDUCTIONS					PAYMENTS		SALARY EXPENSE	
INCOME TAX	SOCIAL SECURITY TAX	MEDICARE TAX		TOTAL	NET AMOUNT	CK. NO.	DEBIT	
								1
								2
								3
								4

PROBLEM 15-4A or 15-4B

	ACCOUNT NAME	TRIAL BALANCE	
		DEBIT	
1	Cash		
2	Accounts Receivable		
3	Merchandise Inventory		
4	Store Supplies		
5	Prepaid Insurance		
6	Store Equipment		
7	Accumulated Depreciation, Store Equipment		
8	Accounts Payable		
9	, Capital		
10	, Drawing		
11	Sales		
12	Sales Returns and Allowances		
13	Purchases		
14	Purchases Returns and Allowances		
15	Purchases Discount		
16	Freight In		
17	Salary Expense		
18	Advertising Expense		
19	Rent Expense		
20			
21	Income Summary		
22	Store Supplies Expense		
23	Insurance Expense		
24	Depreciation Expense, Store Equipment		
25	Salaries Payable		
26			
27	Net Loss		
28			
29			
30			
31			
32			
33			

ADJUSTMENTS		INCOME STATEMENT		BALANCE SHEET		
DEBIT	CREDIT	DEBIT	CREDIT	DEBIT	CREDIT	
						1
						2
						3
						4
						5
						6
						7
						8
						9
						10
						11
						12
						13
						14
						15
						16
						17
						18
						19
						20
						21
						22
						23
						24
						25
						26
						27
						28
						29
						30
						31
						32
						33
						34
						35
						36

PROBLEM 14-2B

	ACCOUNT NAME	TRIAL BAL. DEBIT				
1	Cash	9	8	5	0	00
2	Accounts Receivable	34	2	0	0	00
3	Merchandise Inventory	48	6	0	0	00
4	Supplies		9	8	0	00
5	Prepaid Insurance		7	2	0	00
6	Store Equipment	17	8	6	0	00
7	Accumulated Depreciation, Store Equipment					
8	Office Equipment	6	4	0	0	00
9	Accumulated Depreciation, Office Equipment					
10	Notes Payable					
11	Accounts Payable					
12	Unearned Rent					
13	H. N. Beal, Capital					
14	H. N. Beal, Drawing	16	0	0	0	00
15	Sales					
16	Sales Returns and Allowances	2	1	4	0	00
17	Purchases	259	6	8	0	00
18	Purchases Returns and Allowances					
19	Purchases Discount					
20	Freight In	1	3	2	0	00
21	Salary Expense	29	5	0	0	00
22	Interest Expense		4	2	0	00
23		427	6	7	0	00
24						
25						
26						
27						
28						
29						
30						
31						
32						
33						

ADJUSTMENTS		INCOME STATEMENT		BALANCE SHEET		
DEBIT	CREDIT	DEBIT	CREDIT	DEBIT	CREDIT	
						1
						2
						3
						4
						5
						6
						7
						8
						9
						10
						11
						12
						13
						14
						15
						16
						17
						18
						19
						20
						21
						22
						23
						24
						25
						26
						27
						28
						29
						30
						31
						32
						33

PROBLEM 14-1A or 14-1B

	ACCOUNT NAME	TRIAL BALA	
		DEBIT	
1			
2			
3			
4			
5			
6			
7			
8			
9			
10			
11			
12			
13			
14			
15			
16			
17			
18			
19			
20			
21			
22			
23			
24			
25			
26			
27			
28			
29			
30			
31			
32			
33			

	DEDUCTIONS					PAYMENTS			
FEDERAL INCOME TAX	STATE INCOME TAX	SOCIAL SECURITY TAX	MEDICARE TAX		TOTAL	NET AMOUNT	CK. NO.	SALARY EXPENSE DEBIT	
									1
									2
									3
									4
									5
									6
									7
									8
									9
									10
									11
									12
									13
									14
									15
									16
									17
									18
									19
									20
									21
									22
									23
									24
									25
									26
									27
									28
									29
									30
									31
									32
									33
									34
									35

NAME _____ DATE _____ CLASS _____

PROBLEM 10-2A or 10-2B

	NAME	BEGINNING CUMULATIVE EARNINGS	TOTAL EARNINGS	ENDING CUMULATIVE EARNINGS	TAXABLE EARNINGS		
					UNEMPLOYMENT	SOCIAL SECURITY	MEDICAF
1							
2							
3							
4							
5							
6							
7							
8							
9							
10							
11							
12							
13							
14							
15							
16							
17							
18							
19							
20							
21							
22							
23							
24							
25							
26							
27							
28							
29							
30							
31							
32							
33							
34							
35							

	ADJUSTMENTS		INCOME STATEMENT		BALANCE SHEET		
	DEBIT	CREDIT	DEBIT	CREDIT	DEBIT	CREDIT	
							1
							2
							3
							4
							5
							6
							7
							8
							9
							10
							11
							12
							13
							14
							15
							16
							17
							18
							19
							20
							21
							22
							23
							24
							25
							26
							27
							28
							29
							30
							31
							32
							33

PROBLEM 14-2A

	ACCOUNT NAME	TRIAL BALANCE	
		DEBIT	CREDIT
1	Cash	17 3 8 8 00	
2	Accounts Receivable	64 4 4 3 00	
3	Merchandise Inventory	182 7 5 7 00	
4	Supplies	2 3 5 5 00	
5	Prepaid Insurance	2 4 4 2 00	
6	Store Equipment	55 3 8 6 00	
7	Accumulated Depreciation, Store Equipment		44 1 3
8	Office Equipment	14 1 5 4 00	
9	Accumulated Depreciation, Office Equipment		2 5 8
10	Notes Payable		6 0 0
11	Accounts Payable		46 2 3
12	Unearned Rent		4 8 0
13	B. N. Hahn, Capital		180 7 9
14	B. N. Hahn, Drawing	42 0 0 0 00	
15	Sales		978 0 0
16	Sales Returns and Allowances	14 6 2 2 00	
17	Purchases	737 3 4 9 00	
18	Purchases Returns and Allowances		20 1 6
19	Purchases Discount		11 4 5
20	Freight In	77 2 9 8 00	
21	Salary Expense	82 8 0 0 00	
22	Interest Expense	1 1 5 8 00	
23		1,294 1 5 2 00	1,294 1 5
24			
25			
26			
27			
28			
29			
30			
31			
32			
33			

		ADJUSTMENTS		INCOME STATEMENT		BALANCE SHEET		
		DEBIT	CREDIT	DEBIT	CREDIT	DEBIT	CREDIT	
								1
								2
								3
								4
								5
0	00							6
								7
0	00							8
0	00							9
0	00							10
0	00							11
0	00							12
								13
0	00							14
								15
								16
								17
0	00							18
0	00							19
								20
								21
								22
0	00							23
								24
								25
								26
								27
								28
								29
								30
								31
								32
								33

PROBLEM 14-4A or 14-4B

ACCOUNT NAME	TRIAL BALANCE	
	DEBIT	CREDIT
1		
2		
3		
4		
5		
6		
7		
8		
9		
10		
11		
12		
13		
14		
15		
16		
17		
18		
19		
20		
21		
22		
23		
24		
25		
26		
27		
28		
29		
30		
31		
32		
33		
34		
35		
36		

		ADJUSTMENTS		INCOME STATEMENT		BALANCE SHEET		
		DEBIT	CREDIT	DEBIT	CREDIT	DEBIT	CREDIT	
								1
								2
								3
								4
								5
								6
								7
								8
								9
								10
								11
								12
								13
								14
								15
								16
								17
								18
								19
								20
								21
								22
								23
								24
								25
								26
								27
								28
								29
								30
								31
								32
								33

COMPREHENSIVE REVIEW PROBLEM

PAYROLL REGISTER FOR SEMIMONTHLY PERIOD

	NAME	TOTAL HOURS	BEGINNING CUMULATIVE EARNINGS	EARNINGS	ENDING CUMULATIVE EARNINGS	TAXABLE EARNINGS UNEMPLOYMENT	TAXABLE EARNINGS SOCIAL SECURITY	MEDIC
1	N. C. Drake	40	—	2730 00	2730 00	2730 00	2730 00	27
2	L. M. Williams	40	—	2240 00	2240 00	2240 00	2240 00	22
3			—	4970 00	4970 00	4970 00	4970 00	49
4								

PAYROLL REGISTER FOR SEMIMONTHLY PERIOD

	NAME	TOTAL HOURS	BEGINNING CUMULATIVE EARNINGS	EARNINGS	ENDING CUMULATIVE EARNINGS	TAXABLE EARNINGS UNEMPLOYMENT	TAXABLE EARNINGS SOCIAL SECURITY	MEDIC
1	N. C. Drake	40	2730 00	2730 00	5460 00	2730 00	2730 00	27
2	L. M. Williams	40	2240 00	2240 00	4480 00	2240 00	2240 00	22
3			4970 00	4970 00	9940 00	4970 00	4970 00	49
4								

PAYROLL REGISTER FOR SEMIMONTHLY PERIOD

	NAME	TOTAL HOURS	BEGINNING CUMULATIVE EARNINGS	EARNINGS	ENDING CUMULATIVE EARNINGS	TAXABLE EARNINGS UNEMPLOYMENT	TAXABLE EARNINGS SOCIAL SECURITY	MEDIC
1								
2								
3								
4								

PAYROLL REGISTER FOR SEMIMONTHLY PERIOD

	NAME	TOTAL HOURS	BEGINNING CUMULATIVE EARNINGS	EARNINGS	ENDING CUMULATIVE EARNINGS	TAXABLE EARNINGS UNEMPLOYMENT	TAXABLE EARNINGS SOCIAL SECURITY	MED
1								
2								
3								
4								

Draperies

k Sheet

d February 28, 19—

		ADJUSTMENTS		INCOME STATEMENT		BALANCE SHEET		
T		DEBIT	CREDIT	DEBIT	CREDIT	DEBIT	CREDIT	
								1
								2
								3
								4
								5
								6
								7
								8
								9
								10
								11
								12
								13
								14
								15
								16
								17
								18
								19
								20
								21
								22
								23
								24
								25
								26
								27
								28
								29
								30
								31
								32
								33
								34
								35

PROBLEM 5-2A

For Mon

ACCOUNT NAME	TRIAL BALANCE DEBIT			TRIAL BALANCE CREDIT			ADJUSTME DEBIT		
1 Cash	1 6 6 2	00							
2 Office Supplies	2 2 6	00							
3 Prepaid Insurance	5 0 5	00							
4 Office Equipment	5 9 9 5	00							
5 Accumulated Depreciation, Office									
6 Equipment				1 9 2 5	00				
7 Office Furniture	1 4 1 0	00							
8 Accumulated Depreciation, Office									
9 Furniture				9 1 5	00				
10 Library	10 9 5 0	00							
11 Accumulated Depreciation, Library				7 8 7 0	00				
12 Accounts Payable				9 4 5	00				
13 R. Jurocich, Capital				7 7 3 3	00				
14 R. Jurocich, Drawing	2 7 6 0	00							
15 Professional Fees				7 1 1 2	00				
16 Salary Expense	1 5 2 0	00							
17 Rent Expense	7 1 5	00							
18 Travel Expense	4 7 4	00							
19 Utilities Expense	8 2	00							
20 Taxes Expense	9 1	00							
21 Miscellaneous Expense	1 1 0	00							
22	26 5 0 0	00		26 5 0 0	00				
23 Office Supplies Expense							(a) 1 2 5	00	
24 Insurance Expense							(b) 9 2	00	
25 Depreciation Expense, Office									
26 Equipment							(c) 8 6	00	
27 Depreciation Expense, Office									
28 Furniture							(d) 4 2	00	
29 Depreciation Expense, Library							(e) 1 5 6	00	
30							5 0 1	00	
31 Net Income									
32									

ADJUSTED TRIAL BALANCE		INCOME STATEMENT		BALANCE SHEET		
DEBIT	CREDIT	DEBIT	CREDIT	DEBIT	CREDIT	
						1
						2
						3
						4
						5
						6
						7
						8
						9
						10
						11
						12
						13
						14
						15
						16
						17
						18
						19
						20
						21
						22
						23
						24
						25
						26
						27
						28
						29
						30
						31
						32

A-1

PROBLEM

PAYROLL REGISTER

	NAME	TOTAL HOURS	BEGINNING CUMULATIVE EARNINGS	TOTAL EARNINGS	ENDING CUMULATIVE EARNINGS	TAXABLE EARNINGS	
						UNEMPLOYMENT	SOCIAL SECURITY
1							
2							
3							
4							
5							
6							
7							
8							
9							
10							
11							
12							
13							
14							
15							
16							
17							
18							
19							
20							
21							
22							
23							
24							
25							
26							
27							
28							
29							
30							
31							
32							
33							
34							
35							

				DEDUCTIONS					PAYMENTS		EXPENSE ACCOUNT DEBITED		
	FEDERAL INCOME TAX	SOCIAL SECURITY TAX	MEDICARE TAX	OTHER		TOTAL		NET AMOUNT	CK. NO.	SALES SALARY EXPENSE	OFFICE SALARY EXPENSE		
				CODE	AMOUNT								
1													
2													
3													
4													
5													
6													
7													
8													
9													
10													
11													
12													
13													
14													
15													
16													
17													
18													
19													
20													
21													
22													
23													
24													
25													
26													
27													
28													
29													
30													
31													
32													
33													
34													
35													

PROBLEM

COMBINED

	CASH							OT
	DEBIT	CREDIT	CK. NO.	DATE	ACCOUNT NAME	POST. REF.	DEBIT	
1								
2								
3								
4								
5								
6								
7								
8								
9								
10								
11								
12								
13								
14								
15								
16								
17								
18								
19								
20								
21								
22								
23								
24								
25								
26								
27								
28								
29								
30								
31								
32								
33								
34								
35								
36								
37								
38								

							1
							2
							3
							4
							5
							6
							7
							8
							9
							10
							11
							12
							13
							14
							15
							16
							17
							18
							19
							20
							21
							22
							23
							24
							25
							26
							27
							28
							29
							30
							31
							32
							33
							34
							35

PROBLEM

	ACCOUNT NAME	TRIAL BALANCE		ADJUSTM
		DEBIT	CREDIT	DEBIT
1				
2				
3				
4				
5				
6				
7				
8				
9				
10				
11				
12				
13				
14				
15				
16				
17				
18				
19				
20				
21				
22				
23				
24				
25				
26				
27				
28				
29				
30				
31				
32				

ADJUSTED TRIAL BALANCE		INCOME STATEMENT		BALANCE SHEET		
DEBIT	CREDIT	DEBIT	CREDIT	DEBIT	CREDIT	
						1
						2
						3
						4
						5
						6
						7
						8
						9
						10
						11
						12
						13
						14
						15
						16
						17
						18
						19
						20
						21
						22
						23
						24
						25
						26
						27
						28
						29
						30
						31
						32

NAME _____ DATE _____ CLASS _____

PROBLEM

	ACCOUNT NAME	TRIAL BALANCE		ADJUSTMENTS	
		DEBIT	CREDIT	DEBIT	CREDIT
1					
2					
3					
4					
5					
6					
7					
8					
9					
10					
11					
12					
13					
14					
15					
16					
17					
18					
19					
20					
21					
22					
23					
24					
25					
26					
27					
28					
29					
30					
31					
32					

		ADJUSTED TRIAL BALANCE		INCOME STATEMENT		BALANCE SHEET		
DIT		DEBIT	CREDIT	DEBIT	CREDIT	DEBIT	CREDIT	
								1
								2
								3
								4
								5
								6
								7
								8
								9
								10
								11
								12
								13
								14
								15
								16
								17
								18
								19
								20
								21
								22
								23
								24
								25
								26
								27
								28
								29
								30
								31
								32

PROBLEM

COMBINED

	CASH		CK. NO.	DATE	ACCOUNT NAME	POST. REF.	OTHER ACCOUNTS	
	DEBIT	CREDIT					DEBIT	CREDIT
1								
2								
3								
4								
5								
6								
7								
8								
9								
10								
11								
12								
13								
14								
15								
16								
17								
18								
19								
20								
21								
22								
23								
24								
25								
26								
27								
28								
29								
30								
31								
32								
33								
34								
35								

TS											
CREDIT		DEBIT		CREDIT							
											1
											2
											3
											4
											5
											6
											7
											8
											9
											10
											11
											12
											13
											14
											15
											16
											17
											18
											19
											20
											21
											22
											23
											24
											25
											26
											27
											28
											29
											30
											31
											32
											33
											34
											35
											36
											37
											38

PROBLEM

PAYROLL REGISTER FOR WEE

	NAME	TOTAL HOURS	BEGINNING CUMULATIVE EARNINGS	TOTAL EARNINGS	ENDING CUMULATIVE EARNINGS	TAXABLE EARNINGS		
						UNEMPLOYMENT	SOCIAL SECURITY	MEDICAR
1								
2								
3								
4								
5								
6								
7								
8								
9								
10								
11								
12								
13								
14								
15								
16								
17								
18								
19								
20								
21								
22								
23								
24								
25								
26								
27								
28								
29								
30								
31								
32								
33								
34								
35								

		DEDUCTIONS						PAYMENTS		EXPENSE ACCOUNT DEBITED	
					OTHER						
ARE	FEDERAL INCOME TAX	SOCIAL SECURITY TAX	MEDICARE TAX	CODE	AMOUNT	TOTAL		NET AMOUNT	CK. NO.	SALES SALARY EXPENSE	OFFICE SALARY EXPENSE	
												1
												2
												3
												4
												5
												6
												7
												8
												9
												10
												11
												12
												13
												14
												15
												16
												17
												18
												19
												20
												21
												22
												23
												24
												25
												26
												27
												28
												29
												30
												31
												32
												33
												34
												35

PROBLEM 5-1A or 5-1B

_____

_____

_____

_____

		TRIAL BALANCE		ADJUSTMENTS	
	ACCOUNT NAME	DEBIT	CREDIT	DEBIT	CREDIT
1					
2					
3					
4					
5					
6					
7					
8					
9					
10					
11					
12					
13					
14					
15					
16					
17					
18					
19					
20					
21					
22					
23					
24					
25					
26					
27					
28					
29					
30					
31					
32					

(prior)	ADJUSTED TRIAL BALANCE		INCOME STATEMENT		BALANCE SHEET		
	DEBIT	CREDIT	DEBIT	CREDIT	DEBIT	CREDIT	
	1662 00				1662 00		1
5 00	101 00				101 00		2
2 00	413 00				413 00		3
	5995 00				5995 00		4
							5
5 00		2011 00				2011 00	6
	1410 00				1410 00		7
							8
2 00		957 00				957 00	9
	10950 00				10950 00		10
5 00		8026 00				8026 00	11
		945 00				945 00	12
		7733 00				7733 00	13
	2760 00				2760 00		14
		7112 00		7112 00			15
	1520 00		1520 00				16
	715 00		715 00				17
	474 00		474 00				18
	82 00		82 00				19
	91 00		91 00				20
	110 00		110 00				21
							22
	125 00		125 00				23
	92 00		92 00				24
							25
	86 00		86 00				26
							27
	42 00		42 00				28
	156 00		156 00				29
00	26784 00	26784 00	3493 00	7112 00	23291 00	19672 00	30
			3619 00			3619 00	31
			7112 00	7112 00	23291 00	23291 00	32

PROBLEM 6-4B

Kap

For Yea

	ACCOUNT NAME	TRIAL BALANCE		ADJUST
		DEBIT	CREDIT	DEBIT
1	Cash	2 2 8 3 00		
2	Accounts Receivable	4 9 7 5 00		
3	Supplies	8 2 1 00		
4	Equipment	7 8 0 1 00		
5	Accumulated Depreciation,			
6	Equipment		3 9 8 8 00	
7	Truck	11 8 7 5 00		
8	Accumulated Depreciation, Truck		9 1 2 0 00	
9	Accounts Payable		2 1 3 8 00	
10	T. A. Kaplan, Capital		6 3 9 4 00	
11	T. A. Kaplan, Drawing	17 9 5 0 00		
12	Service Income		40 9 0 5 00	
13	Wages Expense	14 1 1 0 00		
14	Advertising Expense	5 2 6 00		
15	Truck Operating Expense	7 5 1 00		
16	Utilities Expense	5 8 3 00		
17	Miscellaneous Expense	8 7 0 00		
18		62 5 4 5 00	62 5 4 5 00	
19				
20				
21				
22				
23				
24				
25				
26				
27				
28				
29				
30				
31				
32				

ADJUSTED TRIAL BALANCE		INCOME STATEMENT		BALANCE SHEET		
DEBIT	CREDIT	DEBIT	CREDIT	DEBIT	CREDIT	
						1
						2
						3
						4
						5
						6
						7
						8
						9
						10
						11
						12
						13
						14
						15
						16
						17
						18
						19
						20
						21
						22
						23
						24
						25
						26
						27
						28
						29
						30
						31
						32

PROBLEM 6-3B

For Year

	ACCOUNT NAME	TRIAL BALANCE DEBIT	TRIAL BALANCE CREDIT	ADJUSTING DEBIT
1	Cash	6 4 2 2 00		
2	Office Supplies	5 9 8 00		
3	Equipment	15 3 8 0 00		
4	Accumulated Depreciation,			
5	Equipment		1 4 2 0 00	
6	L. H. Patten, Capital		12 3 4 5 00	
7	L. H. Patten, Drawing	20 6 0 0 00		
8	Fees Earned		58 6 0 0 00	
9	Salary Expense	20 4 0 0 00		(c) 6 2 5 00
10	Rent Expense	6 3 0 0 00		
11	Telephone Expense	9 1 1 00		
12	Advertising Expense	9 7 9 00		
13	Miscellaneous Expense	7 7 5 00		
14		72 3 6 5 00	72 3 6 5 00	
15	Office Supplies Expense			(a) 2 7 8 00
16	Depreciation Expense, Equipment			(b) 1 2 3 5 00
17	Salaries Payable			
18				2 1 3 8 00
19	Net Income			
20				
21				
22				
23				
24				
25				
26				
27				
28				
29				
30				
31				
32				

	ADJUSTED TRIAL BALANCE		INCOME STATEMENT		BALANCE SHEET		
	DEBIT	CREDIT	DEBIT	CREDIT	DEBIT	CREDIT	
	7 2 3 1 20				7 2 3 1 20		1
	1 5 4 80				1 5 4 80		2
	6 8 2 0 00				6 8 2 0 00		3
							4
		1 8 2 4 40				1 8 2 4 40	5
		13 4 6 0 00				13 4 6 0 00	6
	25 7 0 0 00				25 7 0 0 00		7
		59 9 2 0 00		59 9 2 0 00			8
	26 0 2 5 00		26 0 2 5 00				9
	5 6 8 0 00		5 6 8 0 00				10
	9 7 2 60		9 7 2 60				11
	1 4 8 0 20		1 4 8 0 20				12
	4 6 5 40		4 6 5 40				13
							14
	3 7 2 20		3 7 2 20				15
	1 0 2 8 00		1 0 2 8 00				16
		7 2 5 00				7 2 5 00	17
	75 9 2 9 40	75 9 2 9 40	36 0 2 3 40	59 9 2 0 00	39 9 0 6 00	16 0 0 9 40	18
			23 8 9 6 60			23 8 9 6 60	19
			59 9 2 0 00	59 9 2 0 00	39 9 0 6 00	39 9 0 6 00	20
							21
							22
							23
							24
							25
							26
							27
							28
							29
							30
							31
							32

PROBLEM 5-4A or 5-4B

	ACCOUNT NAME	TRIAL BALANCE		ADJUST
		DEBIT	CREDIT	DEBIT
1				
2				
3				
4				
5				
6				
7				
8				
9				
10				
11				
12				
13				
14				
15				
16				
17				
18				
19				
20				
21				
22				
23				
24				
25				
26				
27				
28				
29				
30				
31				
32				

ADJUSTED TRIAL BALANCE		INCOME STATEMENT		BALANCE SHEET		
DEBIT	CREDIT	DEBIT	CREDIT	DEBIT	CREDIT	
						1
						2
						3
						4
						5
						6
						7
						8
						9
						10
						11
						12
						13
						14
						15
						16
						17
						18
						19
						20
						21
						22
						23
						24
						25
						26
						27
						28
						29
						30
						31
						32

PROBLEM 5-3A

Spr

For Mont

	ACCOUNT NAME	TRIAL BALANCE				ADJUSTME
		DEBIT		CREDIT		DEBIT
1	Cash	1 9 9 2 00				
2	Supplies	9 8 6 00				
3	Prepaid Insurance	7 2 5 00				
4	Land	21 0 0 0 00				
5	Building	95 3 4 0 00				
6	Accumulated Depreciation, Building			44 5 0 0 00		
7	Game Equipment	85 6 1 0 00				
8	Accumulated Depreciation, Game					
9	Equipment			54 8 0 0 00		
10	Furniture and Fixtures	1 2 5 0 00				
11	Accumulated Depreciation, Furniture					
12	and Fixtures			6 8 0 00		
13	Accounts Payable			4 8 1 0 00		
14	Mortgage Payable			62 0 0 0 00		
15	R. C. Springer, Capital			33 9 3 8 00		
16	R. C. Springer, Drawing	2 2 6 0 00				
17	Video Games Income			32 4 6 9 00		
18	Concession Income			2 8 8 0 00		
19	Wages Expense	17 9 5 0 00				
20	Advertising Expense	4 1 2 0 00				
21	Repair Expense	2 5 6 2 00				
22	Utilities Expense	1 7 7 0 00				
23	Miscellaneous Expense	5 1 2 00				
24		236 0 7 7 00		236 0 7 7 00		
25						
26						
27						
28						
29						
30						
31						
32						

	ADJUSTED TRIAL BALANCE		INCOME STATEMENT		BALANCE SHEET	
	DEBIT	CREDIT	DEBIT	CREDIT	DEBIT	CREDIT
1	1820 00				1820 00	
2	233 00				233 00	
3	363 00				363 00	
4	6720 00				6720 00	
5						
6		1696 00				1696 00
7	1218 00				1218 00	
8						
9		893 00				893 00
10	1204 00				11204 00	
11		8080 00				8080 00
12		898 00				898 00
13		7651 00				7651 00
14	1550 00				1550 00	
15		7270 00		7270 00		
16	1475 00		1475 00			
17	695 00		695 00			
18	398 00		398 00			
19	72 00		72 00			
20	95 00		95 00			
21	120 00		120 00			
22						
23	117 00		117 00			
24	112 00		112 00			
25						
26	111 00		111 00			
27						
28	25 00		25 00			
29	160 00		160 00			
30	26488 00	26488 00	3380 00	7270 00	23108 00	19218 00
31			3890 00			3890 00
32			7270 00	7270 00	23108 00	23108 00

PROBLEM 5-2B

T.C. Dorman, At

Work S

For Month Ended

ACCOUNT NAME	TRIAL BALANCE DEBIT	TRIAL BALANCE CREDIT	ADJUSTMENTS DEBIT	ADJUSTMENTS CREDIT
1 Cash	1 8 2 0 00			
2 Office Supplies	3 5 0 00			(a) 1 1 7
3 Prepaid Insurance	4 7 5 00			(b) 1 1 2
4 Office Equipment	6 7 2 0 00			
5 Accumulated Depreciation, Office				
6 Equipment		1 5 8 5 00		(c) 1 1 1
7 Office Furniture	1 2 1 8 00			
8 Accumulated Depreciation, Office				
9 Furniture		8 6 8 00		(d) 2 5
10 Library	11 2 0 4 00			
11 Accumulated Depreciation, Library		7 9 2 0 00		(e) 1 6 0
12 Accounts Payable		8 9 8 00		
13 T. C. Dorman, Capital		7 6 5 1 00		
14 T. C. Dorman, Drawing	1 5 5 0 00			
15 Professional Fees		7 2 7 0 00		
16 Salary Expense	1 4 7 5 00			
17 Rent Expense	6 9 5 00			
18 Travel Expense	3 9 8 00			
19 Utilities Expense	7 2 00			
20 Taxes Expense	9 5 00			
21 Miscellaneous Expense	1 2 0 00			
22	26 1 9 2 00	26 1 9 2 00		
23 Office Supplies Expense			(a) 1 1 7 00	
24 Insurance Expense			(b) 1 1 2 00	
25 Depreciation Expense, Office				
26 Equipment			(c) 1 1 1 00	
27 Depreciation Expense, Office				
28 Furniture			(d) 2 5 00	
29 Depreciation Expense, Library			(e) 1 6 0 00	
30			5 2 5 00	5 2
31 Net Income				
32				

ideo Games

Sheet

d August 31, 19—

	ADJUSTED TRIAL BALANCE		INCOME STATEMENT		BALANCE SHEET		
	DEBIT	CREDIT	DEBIT	CREDIT	DEBIT	CREDIT	
							1
							2
							3
							4
							5
							6
							7
							8
							9
							10
							11
							12
							13
							14
							15
							16
							17
							18
							19
							20
							21
							22
							23
							24
							25
							26
							27
							28
							29
							30
							31
							32

PROBLEM 5-3B

Elliott Luxu

Work S

For Month Ended

ACCOUNT NAME	TRIAL BALANCE		ADJUSTMENTS	
	DEBIT	CREDIT	DEBIT	CREDIT
1 Cash	2 995 00			
2 Supplies	962 00			
3 Prepaid Insurance	675 00			
4 Land	21 000 00			
5 Building	184 200 00			
6 Accumulated Depreciation, Building		26 000 00		
7 Bowling Equipment	90 315 00			
8 Accumulated Depreciation, Bowling				
9 Equipment		61 200 00		
10 Furniture and Fixtures	9 700 00			
11 Accumulated Depreciation, Furniture				
12 and Fixtures		4 420 00		
13 Accounts Payable		5 313 00		
14 Mortgage Payable		58 000 00		
15 D. R. Elliott, Capital		147 953 00		
16 D. R. Elliott, Drawing	6 100 00			
17 Bowling Fees Income		44 112 00		
18 Concession Income		6 328 00		
19 Wages Expense	27 300 00			
20 Advertising Expense	4 204 00			
21 Repair Expense	3 473 00			
22 Utilities Expense	1 820 00			
23 Miscellaneous Expense	582 00			
24	353 326 00	353 326 00		
25				
26				
27				
28				
29				
30				
31				
32				

T		ADJUSTED TRIAL BALANCE			INCOME STATEMENT			BALANCE SHEET		
		DEBIT	CREDIT		DEBIT	CREDIT		DEBIT	CREDIT	
											1
											2
											3
											4
											5
											6
											7
											8
											9
											10
											11
											12
											13
											14
											15
											16
											17
											18
											19
											20
											21
											22
											23
											24
											25
											26
											27
											28
											29
											30
											31
											32

PROBLEM 6-3A

Lakeview Insu

Work

For Year Ended De

	ACCOUNT NAME	TRIAL BALANCE DEBIT	TRIAL BALANCE CREDIT	ADJUSTMENTS DEBIT	ADJUSTMENTS CREDIT
1	Cash	7 2 3 1 20			
2	Office Supplies	5 2 7 00			(a) 3 7 2
3	Equipment	6 8 2 0 00			
4	Accumulated Depreciation,				
5	Equipment		7 9 6 40		(b) 1 0 2 8
6	S. P. Watanabe, Capital		13 4 6 0 00		
7	S. P. Watanabe, Drawing	25 7 0 0 00			
8	Commissions Earned		59 9 2 0 00		
9	Salary Expense	25 3 0 0 00		(c) 7 2 5 00	
10	Rent Expense	5 6 8 0 00			
11	Telephone Expense	9 7 2 60			
12	Advertising Expense	1 4 8 0 20			
13	Miscellaneous Expense	4 6 5 40			
14		74 1 7 6 40	74 1 7 6 40		
15	Office Supplies Expense			(a) 3 7 2 20	
16	Depreciation Expense, Equipment			(b) 1 0 2 8 00	
17	Salaries Payable				(c) 7 2 5
18				2 1 2 5 20	2 1 2 5
19	Net Income				
20					
21					
22					
23					
24					
25					
26					
27					
28					
29					
30					
31					
32					

(partial)	ADJUSTED TRIAL BALANCE DEBIT	ADJUSTED TRIAL BALANCE CREDIT	INCOME STATEMENT DEBIT	INCOME STATEMENT CREDIT	BALANCE SHEET DEBIT	BALANCE SHEET CREDIT	
	6 4 2 2 00				6 4 2 2 00		1
8 00	3 2 0 00				3 2 0 00		2
	15 3 8 0 00				15 3 8 0 00		3
							4
5 00		2 6 5 5 00				2 6 5 5 00	5
		12 3 4 5 00				12 3 4 5 00	6
	20 6 0 0 00				20 6 0 0 00		7
		58 6 0 0 00		58 6 0 0 00			8
	21 0 2 5 00		21 0 2 5 00				9
	6 3 0 0 00		6 3 0 0 00				10
	9 1 1 00		9 1 1 00				11
	9 7 9 00		9 7 9 00				12
	7 7 5 00		7 7 5 00				13
							14
	2 7 8 00		2 7 8 00				15
	1 2 3 5 00		1 2 3 5 00				16
5 00		6 2 5 00				6 2 5 00	17
8 00	74 2 2 5 00	74 2 2 5 00	31 5 0 3 00	58 6 0 0 00	42 7 2 2 00	15 6 2 5 00	18
			27 0 9 7 00			27 0 9 7 00	19
			58 6 0 0 00	58 6 0 0 00	42 7 2 2 00	42 7 2 2 00	20

PROBLEM 6-4A

Perrini Jani
Work
For Year Ended

	ACCOUNT NAME	TRIAL BALANCE		ADJUSTMENTS	
		DEBIT	CREDIT	DEBIT	CREDIT
1	Cash	4 7 2 5 50			
2	Accounts Receivable	4 3 1 0 00			
3	Cleaning Supplies	5 3 5 50			
4	Cleaning Equipment	6 7 2 0 00			
5	Accumulated Depreciation, Cleaning				
6	Equipment		4 1 2 0 00		
7	Truck	8 3 9 8 00			
8	Accumulated Depreciation, Truck		3 8 7 2 00		
9	Accounts Payable		1 8 5 5 00		
10	P. N. Perrini, Capital		10 1 9 9 00		
11	P. N. Perrini, Drawing	16 4 5 0 00			
12	Service Income		34 2 2 2 00		
13	Wages Expense	11 2 5 0 00			
14	Advertising Expense	5 2 3 50			
15	Truck Operating Expense	7 5 1 00			
16	Utilities Expense	4 1 9 50			
17	Miscellaneous Expense	1 8 5 00			
18		54 2 6 8 00	54 2 6 8 00		
19					
20					
21					
22					
23					
24					
25					
26					
27					
28					
29					
30					
31					
32					

	ADJUSTED TRIAL BALANCE		INCOME STATEMENT		BALANCE SHEET		
	DEBIT	CREDIT	DEBIT	CREDIT	DEBIT	CREDIT	
							1
							2
							3
							4
							5
							6
							7
							8
							9
							10
							11
							12
							13
							14
							15
							16
							17
							18
							19
							20
							21
							22
							23
							24
							25
							26
							27
							28
							29
							30
							31
							32